EVERYTHING ABOUT
ASTRONAUTS

EVERYTHING ABOUT
ASTRONAUTS

FASCINATING FUN FACTS AND TRIVIA ABOUT ASTRONAUTS FOR TEENS AND ADULTS

by
MARIANNE JENNINGS

KNB

DEDICATION

For my nieces and nephews.

May you stay curious, keep reaching for the stars and know that the impossible is indeed possible.

Copyright and Disclaimer

Everything About Astronauts Vol. 2:
Fascinating Fun Facts and Trivia about Astronauts for Teens and Adults

Knowledge Nuggets Series by Marianne Jennings

Edited by Karina Hamalainen, Joe Levit, and Skye Loyd.
Fact checked and indexed by Hank Musolf
Cover design by Matt Davies
Interior design and formatting by Bea Reis Custodio
Proofread by Bill Siever

While all attempts have been made to verify the information provided in this publication, neither the author nor the publisher assumes any responsibility for errors, omissions, or contrary interpretations on the subject matter herein. This book is for entertainment purposes only. The views expressed are those of the author alone, and should not be taken as expert instruction or commands. The reader is responsible for his or her own actions.

Library of Congress Control Number: 2021922477
ISBN 978-1-7342456-6-0 (paperback)
ISBN 978-1-7342456-7-7 (ebook)

Trademarks that are mentioned are done without written consent and can in no way be considered an endorsement from the trademark holder.

Disclaimer: No astronauts were harmed during the making of this book.

CONTENTS

FREE BONUS

As a **special bonus** and as a **thank you** for purchasing this book, I'm giving you a free download of my award-winning book:

So You Think You Know CANADA, Eh?
Fascinating Fun Facts and Trivia about Canada for the Entire Family.

How much DO YOU REALLY KNOW about Canada?
Discover fascinating fun facts and trivia and test your knowledge of Canada and quiz your friends.

It's all **FREE.**

Download your bonus fun fact e-book here:

https://bit.ly/astronautbook2-bonus

Enjoy!

HOW TO READ THIS BOOK

This book is divided into topics, and the facts are in bite-size nuggets. There is no need to read this book cover to cover. Just pick a subject that seems interesting and jump right in!

Glossary
There are several acronyms and a few technical terms throughout this book. Please refer to the glossary found at the end of the book to find definitions and short explanations.

Index
If there's a particular topic or person you'd like to learn more about, please refer to the index at the very back of the book.

Quiz Yourself
To test yourself and your friends with what you've learned, you'll find a fun, short quiz with answers in the back.

Please Bookmark the RESOURCES Page so you can easily access all the videos, images, and other resources mentioned throughout this book with direct links to each.

KnowledgeNuggetBooks.com/resources

INTRODUCTION

Astronauts are awesome. Ever since I learned that men and women could get a job that allowed them to fly into outer space, I have been fascinated and intrigued by the profession, the science that put them there and the men and women themselves who see our Earth from above.

I have never lived in a world where humans weren't exploring space, and today we live in a world where people beyond just professional astronauts are flying into space. As I write this, Virgin Galactic and Amazon's Blue Origin have both sent nonprofessional astronauts into space in their commercial spaceships. Currently, men and women are training to return to the Moon in the next several years. Soon, women too will have walked on the Moon. And it may not be too much longer before we send humans to Mars.

These are exciting and adventurous times, and there is renewed interest in space exploration and the people who do it.

This book was originally one very long book, but to make it easier to digest, it has been broken up into volumes. Volume 1 covers mostly astronaut topics that are about famous astronauts and about things that take place "on the ground," where Volume 2 covers mostly astronaut life "up in space." With everything that is happening now and in the next few years, you can expect a Volume 3 in the future.

This book is for those who share the love, curiosity and excitement about all things astronauts. I hope you enjoy reading, and will find some fun facts, stories and astronaut trivia that will excite you, cause you to wonder and make you say, "Wow, I didn't know that!"

Never stop learning.

Marianne

ASTRONAUT TRADITIONS & SUPERSTITIONS

Russian Cosmonaut Superstitions and Traditions

RUSSIA'S IMPRESSIVE SPACEFLIGHT SAFETY RECORD

In the entire history of Soviet and Russian spaceflight—as far as we know—only four cosmonauts have died during a mission. The first was Soyuz 1 pilot Vladimir Komarov, in 1967. The other three were the crew of Soyuz 11 in 1971. No other country involved in spaceflight has such a remarkable safety record.

If something was done a particular way and was successful, then it makes sense that it should be kept that way for the next time. Why fix what works?

This is Russia's philosophy and it seems to be working for them. There are very specific traditions and routines that every crew follows for every launch. Some of these traditions are over 50 years old, and started when Yuri Gagarin became the first person in space in 1961.

NO LAUNCHES ON OCTOBER 24TH

Because two accidents took place in Baikonur on October 24 (in 1960, and 1963), no launches are ever scheduled for that day.

FLOWERS FOR YURI GAGARIN & SERGEI KOROLEV

Crew members visit Red Square in Moscow to honor the legacy of both Yuri Gagarin and Sergei Korolev. Gagarin was the first person to go into space (1961). Sergei Korolev was the designer of the early Soviet rockets, and is considered the father of Russia's space program. Each crew member, and their backup crew, lays a single carnation at the foot of the Kremlin wall, where Gagarin and Korolev's remains are interred.[1]

PLANTING A TREE

Before Yuri Gagarin became the first human in space, he planted a tree in what is now known as Cosmonaut Alley in Baikonur, Kazakhstan. Every person who has flown from the cosmodrome has planted a tree before launching. Today, there is a grove of trees.

The grove is behind the Cosmonaut Hotel, and lines what is known as the Avenue of Cosmonauts. Each tree has a plaque in front of it, with the name of the crew member and the year.

Gagarin's tree still stands today, and is the tallest. The trees commemorate those who made it into space, but also act as a living memorial to those who didn't make it back.[2]

RAISING THE FLAG

About five days before launch, a flag-raising ceremony is held in Baikonur. The crew raises a flag for each of the countries participating in the next launch to the International Space Station.

LEAVING THEIR MARK

Crew members leave their mark in all sorts of places. In keeping with tradition, all crew members sign the guest book in Yuri Gagarin's office, which has been preserved as a museum in Star City outside of Moscow. They also sign a wall in the museum at Baikonur and the door of their bedroom at the Cosmonaut Hotel in Kazakhstan.

As with tradition, Commander Chris Hadfield signs the door of his room at the Cosmonaut Hotel before launching into space onboard the Soyuz. Photo courtesy of NASA/Carla Cioffi.

Upon returning home, the cosmonauts and astronauts will often sign the charred outer casing of the space capsule and the inside of the recovery helicopter.[3]

8 HOURS BEFORE LAUNCH

The Soyuz rocket is transferred from its hangar to the launchpad by train. While it's considered bad luck for the crew to watch the Soyuz rollout, it's considered good luck for spectators to place coins on the track, which get flattened by the incoming train. Luckily, this tradition has not led to any injury or derailments.

Instead of watching the rocket rollout, each Soyuz crewmember gets a haircut. For some, this is the last haircut they get until they return to Earth. Some older cosmonauts refuse to cut their hair while in space. Cosmonaut Sasha Kaleri was cutting his hair when a fire started onboard the space station Mir, and the act has been thought to be unlucky ever since.[4]

Soyuz rocket rolled out to launchpad by train. Photo courtesy of NASA.[5]

DID YOU KNOW?

The Soyuz spacecraft and rocket combination are assembled horizontally and rolled out to the launchpad that way. Only after it reaches the launchpad, the orientation is changed to a vertical setup just days before launch.

This is very different than how the space shuttle or the massive Apollo/Saturn spacecrafts were rolled out. NASA vehicles are rolled out while pointing vertically and are carefully balanced on an enormous crawler transport.[6]

MOVIE NIGHT

The night before launch, the cosmonauts watch the 1969 film *White Sun of the Desert*. This is a Russian classic and is a Russian twist on the American western. Every astronaut who has flown from Baikonur has watched this film the night before launch.[7]

PRE-FLIGHT ENEMA

On average, cosmonauts are in their spacesuits for about 10 hours on launch day. While cosmonauts wear adult diapers during launch, most cosmonauts get enemas to help "clear the pipes" before launch to make sure they only pee in those diapers.[8]

ONE LAST EARTHLY SHOWER

Before dressing in their sterile white long johns and long-sleeved underwear, cosmonauts shower using special antimicrobial soap and dry off with a sterile towel.[9]

ALCOHOL SWAB DOWN

To ensure all germs are killed before heading off into space, the Russian flight surgeon wipes down the cosmonauts with alcohol wipes after their shower.[10]

BREAKFAST CEREMONY IN STAR CITY

Traditionally, the last meal before launch is shared with the backup crew and the Russian flight surgeon. They chow down on a selection of bread, ham, eggs, cheese, jam or fruit, bacon, *kasha*, (hot cereal, made with grains boiled in milk) and Russian tea.

MOMENT OF SILENCE

This isn't just a tradition that happens before launch; it's a common Russian superstition. Before leaving for a long journey, everyone sits in silence for a moment. This will happen before the crew leaves the breakfast ceremony.

ANTHEM PLAYED AS THE CREW LEAVES HOTEL

The 1983 Soviet-era rock song *The Grass by the Home* was named the official cosmonaut anthem in 2009. It's sung by the band Zemlyane, which means "The Earthlings" in Russian. The song's lyrics are about a cosmonaut's love for Earth.[11]

RUSSIAN ORTHODOX BLESSING

On the steps of the Cosmonaut Hotel, a Russian Orthodox priest blesses both the Soyuz rocket and the crew. This tradition was started in 1994 by cosmonaut Aleksandr Viktorenko, who requested a blessing before the Soyuz TM-20 crew's launch to the space station Mir.[12]

HORSESHOES FOR GOOD LUCK

The buses that take the crew to Building 254, where they suit up, and then to the launchpad are both adorned with horseshoes.[13][14]

LAST STOP FOR A PIT STOP

Rumor says that Yuri Gagarin had to urinate one last time as they were on the bus to the launchpad for his historic flight in 1961. He chose to urinate on the back-right tire of the bus, and the tradition was born. Female cosmonauts are excused from this tradition, but many have been known to carry bottles of their urine and pour it over the tire to keep with the spirit of the tradition.

SAME LAUNCHPAD
If it was good enough for the first man in space, it's good enough now. Since April 12, 1961, all Soyuz launches happen at the Baikonur Cosmodrome in Kazakhstan.

ONE LAST WAVE GOODBYE
The last ritual before liftoff is when the cosmonauts walk up the first few stairs to the elevator and then turn to wave goodbye to the assembled crowd. It's one last wave to the people of Earth.

PICK YOUR THREE LIFT-OFF SONGS
Each cosmonaut can pick three songs that will be played into the Soyuz capsule before liftoff. Some common songs cosmonauts have played are "Rocket Man" by Elton John, "Don't Stop Me Now" by Queen, "Time to Say Goodbye" by Sarah Brightman, "A Sky Full of Stars" by Coldplay, "Beautiful Day" by U2, "Oh What a Night" by Frankie Valli and The Four Seasons and "The Final Countdown" by Europe.[15]

This tradition started at the very beginning with Yuri Gagarin. The music he chose to play over the intercom was a record of Russian love songs.

SOYUZ SEATING ARRANGEMENTS
Each of the three seats in the Soyuz capsule are assigned and entering the Soyuz is done in a specific order. The first person in the capsule is the left-seater, then the right-seater comes next and finally the Soyuz commander sits in the middle.[16]

NO COUNTDOWNS
Many of us associate a good old-fashioned countdown with rocket launches. But the Russians do things a little differently. Instead of a countdown, the crew inside the Soyuz hears the final launch sequence checklist. This clues them in to when launch will occur.

PUSK & POEKHALI!
Launch happens when the Russian word "pusk" is said by Mission

Control. This translates into "start." Next the crew calls out "Poekhali" which means "Let's go!" If it was good enough for the first man launched into space, tradition has it that it's worth repeating.[17]

NASA Astronaut Superstitions and Traditions

PRE-LAUNCH QUARANTINE

Astronauts quarantine before launch to make sure they aren't sick before they head into space. The length of quarantine varies, but it is usually around two weeks. Quarantine before launch is important due to the nature of spaceflight. The confined area of a spacecraft, recirculated air, not being able to wash your hands often and crew members all touching the same surfaces all create ideal conditions for germs to spread quickly and easily.

Pre-launch quarantine became a requirement after the three crew members of Apollo 7 all developed serious head colds while in space in 1968. Commander Wally Schirra came down with the cold first and then passed it to Walt Cunningham. Finally, Donn Eisele got sick. All astronauts and cosmonauts quarantine before launching into space.[18]

STEAK AND EGGS FOR BREAKFAST

Alan Shepard, the first American to fly into space, ate steak and eggs the morning before his launch. This high protein breakfast made it less likely he would need to relieve himself over the next several hours. While it didn't keep Shepard from peeing in his suit, it did keep him from having to go number 2. Many astronauts over the years have followed his lead by eating steak and eggs for breakfast before their launch.[19]

In May of 2020, NASA astronaut Doug Hurley—who was one of two astronauts to launch into space on the SpaceX Crew Dragon Demo-2 mission—tweeted out a picture of his last meal on Earth. It was a picture of steak and eggs on a NASA-branded plate![20]

CREW STARRING IN SCI-FI MOVIE POSTERS

Expedition crew posters[21] and fact sheets featuring the crew have been created by NASA since the first expedition to the International Space Station in 2000. As the years went by, NASA decided to get a little creative and add a sense of humor to these posters.[22] Many newer posters have taken inspiration from sci-fi movie posters we know and love. They have simply added in the astronauts:

Ocean's 11 was the theme for the crew onboard Space Shuttle *Atlantis* on the STS-125 mission.

Expedition 16's poster took *The Matrix* to a whole new level.[23]

Expedition 42 was featured on a poster that was inspired by *The Hitchhiker's Guide to the Galaxy*.[24] (For those who know, you'll understand why 42 is a significant number here!)

Expedition 45 found themselves with their very own light sabers on a *Star Wars*-inspired poster.[25]

Pirates of the Caribbean became "Pilots Over the Caribbean" for **Expedition 30**.[26]

Star Trek has been the theme for a few different expeditions, including **Expeditions 21** and **134**.

You can see some of the posters from the space shuttle era here: https://www.nasa.gov/centers/kennedy/shuttleoperations/posters.html

You can check out the posters from the International Space Station Expeditions at: https://www.nasa.gov/directorates/heo/sfa/sp/expedition-posters-1-9

ASTRONAUTS WAVING

Believe it or not, the astronauts are taught how to wave before launch! The reason is so that they don't accidently block their face or the face of another crew member and ruin what could have been a great photo before they head off into space. If you watch videos or look at photos of the crews waving, you'll notice that they wave their hands lower than usual.

Expedition 16 Crew Poster. Photo courtesy of NASA.[27]

WHAT DO YOU CALL THE VAN THAT TAKES ASTRONAUTS TO THE LAUNCHPAD?

It's like a joke you'd find on the back of a Laffy Taffy candy wrapper, but what do you call the van that takes astronauts from the quarantine facility to the launchpad? The Astrovan! That's no joke—the Astrovan is its actual name!

ASTROVAN UPGRADE

Recently, some astronauts who have launched into space onboard the SpaceX Crew Dragon spacecrafts have been driven to their launchpad via Tesla cars.[28]

THE LAST BATHROOM ON EARTH

While waiting high up (195 feet or 59 meters) on the launchpad before getting into the space shuttle, astronauts had one last opportunity to use the toilet. After that it's go in your diaper, or wait until you make it into space and can use the toilet in the space shuttle.

JAWS OF DEATH ZIPPER

The space shuttle launch suits had big industrial-size zippers in the front. They were nicknamed the jaws of death by male astronauts. The zippers were designed to hold in air pressure. You don't want to imagine what might happen if a male astronaut lost his grip on that zipper and it zipped shut with great force while he was in the middle of going to the bathroom![29]

THE LAST PHONE CALL

There wasn't just a bathroom on the launchpad for the space shuttle. While waiting for each crew member to use the bathroom and to board the shuttle, there was also a phone. Some used it to make one last call to loved ones. Others used it to order a pizza for the launch director. Pizza deliveries happened more than once![30]

COMMANDER IN FIRST

Boarding the shuttle was a highly choreographed event and there was a specific order in which everyone would board. Since the commander's seat was farthest from the shuttle door, the commander always crawled into the shuttle first.

A KISS & NOTE FROM THEIR SPOUSE

Strapping astronauts into their seats on the space shuttle took about an hour. Once the crew were inside and buckled up, a NASA worker would do one final check to make sure everyone was strapped in securely. Astronaut Chris Hadfield has shared that sometimes during that final check, the worker would give the astronauts a kiss on the forehead and/or a note from their spouse or significant other.[31]

NEWEST PRE-FLIGHT TRADITIONS
Astronauts Doug Hurley and Bob Behnken were the first crew to fly in a SpaceX Dragon capsule, on top of a Falcon rocket that launched in May 2020. The SpaceX Demo-2 mission marked the first time astronauts have launched on American soil since the space shuttle was retired in 2011. Hurley and Behnken got to choose which preflight traditions they wanted to continue or start fresh.[32]

PLANTING TREES
Before launching from American soil, astronaut Bob Behnken planted a lemon tree at his home in Houston, Texas. Planting a tree is one of Russia's cosmonaut preflight traditions and one that Behnken wanted to adopt.

TAGGING THE SIMULATOR
A new preflight tradition that Doug Hurley adopted from his time as a test pilot in the U.S. Marine Corps is something he calls "tagging." Basically, you put a sticker on the mission simulator when you complete your training. To kick off the new tradition, Hurley and Behnken both put the Demo-2 sticker on the SpaceX simulator in Houston.

Kennedy Space Center & Mission Control Launch Traditions
Traditions don't just happen for the astronauts and cosmonauts. Hundreds of people are involved in these launches and space flights. It makes sense that they'd have a few traditions of their own!

THE PEANUT TRADITION

This tradition goes back to the 1960s, during the Ranger missions.[33] These were America's first attempts to take close-up photos of the surface of the Moon. These spacecrafts flew straight into the Moon and would take and send images back to Earth right up until the moment of impact. The first six Rangers failed for a variety of reasons. On the 7th launch, someone brought peanuts into Mission Control and the mission succeeded. It's been a tradition to have peanuts in Mission Control since then.[34]

A NEW HOMEMADE WAISTCOAT FOR EVERY LAUNCH

Gene Kranz, the legendary flight director who led the mission control team to save the crew of Apollo 13, is also famous for having a new homemade waistcoat or vest for each mission.

During his time at NASA, there were three Mission Control teams: red, white, and blue. Kranz was on the white mission control team. Since he liked wearing three-piece suits, his wife decided to make him a white vest. He wore his first white vest when he served as flight controller for Gemini IV on June 3, 1965. Since that first launch, his wife made a new white vest for every launch, and a colorful one to wear to celebrate a successful splashdown and recovery.[35]

THE CUTTING OF THE TIE

After a successful launch, a Kennedy Space Center manager uses scissors to hack off a rookie's necktie just below the knot in front of the entire launch team. This practice is common among aviators after their first solo flight. It has now been borrowed and practiced with rookie launch directors, engineers and NASA test directors.

DONUTS AND BAGELS FOR SHUTTLE ROLLOUT

To celebrate the Shuttle's trip—or roll over—from one facility to the Vehicle Assembly Building (VAC), a NASA flow manager brought in donuts. After a while, the team brought in bagels too.

BEANS AND CORNBREAD AFTER LAUNCH

Since the first shuttle liftoff of STS-1 in 1981, launch controllers have enjoyed beans and cornbread after a successful launch. This tradition started with Former NASA Test Director Chief Norm Carlson, when he brought in a small crock pot of northern beans for his staff. The tradition has become so popular that in 2001, it had expanded to cooking up twelve 18-quart slow cookers full of beans!

The Kennedy Space Center featured the recipe for both the beans and the cornbread in their April 12, 2001, Spaceport Newsletter. This was a special edition marking the 20-year anniversary of the first shuttle launch on April 12, 1981.[36]

Here are those recipes:

Successful Launch Beans

Courtesy of Norm Carlson, former NASA Test Director Chief

Put 6 lbs. of dried Great Northern Beans in an 18-quart electric cooker.

Cut 10 lbs. of smoked ham into cubes.

Add ham and ham bones to beans.

Add ½ shaker of lemon pepper.

Add 3 lbs. chopped onions.

Add 2 stalks chopped celery.

Add 1 tsp. liquid smoke.

Cover with water and cook for at least 8 hours. Enjoy!

Famous Launch Day Cornbread

Martha White Self-Rising Corn Muffin Mix

Follow directions on the box. (This is the actual text that appeared in the April 2001 Spaceport Newsletter.)

International Space Station Traditions

BREAD-AND-SALT WELCOME

This tradition first made its way into outer space onboard the Russian space station Mir. Visitors to today's International Space Station are still offered bread and salt, although the dish may look a little different than what it would on Earth.

Regular table salt and crumbly bread are not allowed in space because they both have a tendency to float away. Wandering crumbs or salt particles could get into the machinery, or the eyes of nearby astronauts! Instead, newcomers are given liquid salt and small chunks of pre-cut bread.[37]

FRIDAY NIGHT IS CULTURE NIGHT!

On Friday nights, the ISS crew get together to eat, watch movies, share unique language expressions (that usually bring a laugh!) and just generally enjoy each other's company.[38] A crew favorite is sharing food that represents the country each crew member is from.

THE CHANGE OF COMMAND CEREMONY

Astronaut Bill Shepherd was the first commander onboard the International Space Station and started a few traditions that are still done today.[39] In the military, there is a change of command ceremony that represents an official transfer of authority and responsibility for a crew.

On the ISS, they hold a broadcasted ceremony where the outgoing space station commander hands over command and "the key to the space station" to the new commander. The key to the space station isn't just symbolic. It's a small physical tool that is used to open the Russian hatches. The key is a recent addition to the tradition and was brought onboard in September 2017 by Expedition 52 cosmonaut commander Fyodor Yurchikhin.[40]

DON'T FORGET TO RING THE BELL!

The first ISS commander, Bill Shepherd, brought a small bell to the ISS and started the tradition of ringing the bell every time a crew departs the ISS. The crew onboard the ISS transmits the ringing bell over the radio while the crew leaves for Earth.[41] This tradition is taken from a Navy ritual where a bell is rung when crews come aboard or depart from another ship.[42] The bell on the ISS is in the Unity node.

Mission stickers inside Node 1 on the International Space Station. Photo courtesy of Google Earth.[43]

LEAVING MISSION STICKERS

Space missions each have their own unique sticker and patch. ISS astronauts leave their mark by putting their mission stickers in Node 1 and in the Airlock. These stickers can be seen on Google Earth view of the International Space Station, which means you can use Google Earth to see them for yourself.[44]

Welcome Home Traditions

BREAD-AND-SALT WELCOME HOME CEREMONY

For Slavic and other cultures, bread symbolizes hospitality and salt symbolizes friendship. To welcome visitors, it's an old tradition to present bread with a ramekin of salt in the middle, served on an embroidered towel. Tradition is to dip a piece of bread into the salt and eat it. Cosmonauts landing back in Kazakhstan are often welcomed home with bread and salt.[45]

Upon their return to Star City, Russia, Expedition 12 crew members are presented with the traditional bread and salt greeting. Photo courtesy of Bill Ingalls/NASA.

ASTRONAUT NESTING DOLLS

This may not be a tradition for all astronauts, but this was a special occasion. Scott Kelly and Mikhail Kornienko spent almost a year in space: 340 days. Scott Kelly broke the American record for longest continuous stay in space. When they returned back to Earth on a Russian Soyuz, they were presented with many gifts. Kelly, Kornienko and their third crew mate, Sergey Volkov, were presented with Russian nesting dolls with the likeness of each astronaut painted on the front.[46]

CARRIED TO CHAIRS

For Soyuz landings on the ground, search and rescue come and retrieve the astronauts and cosmonauts from the capsule. After retrieving the astronauts from the capsule, they're carried to nearby recliners or camp chairs where they can take some time to adjust to Earth's gravity.[47]

POST-FLIGHT MEDICAL CHECKS

As soon as possible, astronauts and cosmonauts get post-landing

Matryoshka Dolls in the likeness of Expedition 57 landing crew members, Serena Auñón-Chancellor, Sergey Prokopyev and Alexander Gerst. Photo courtesy of Bill Ingalls/NASA.

medical checks. If they land in the middle of nowhere, the ground crew sets up inflatable pop-up tents where the astronauts can be checked over by their flight surgeons.[48] Tests are done to check their balance, coordination and ability to walk. The astronauts are asked to run around, jump and stand up from a sitting position. These medical checks take about an hour.[49]

CALLING HOME
One of the first things the astronauts do when they land is to make sure the search and rescue teams know where they are so they can be rescued. The next is to call home using the satellite phone that is part of the equipment in the capsule.

NOTES
1.   Jeffrey Kluger, "Visiting Yuri Gagarin: A Pre-Flight Ritual," Time.com (Time, February 26, 2016), https://time.com/4238910/gagarin-red-square-ritual/.

2. Allison C. Meier, "Cosmonaut Grove," Atlas Obscura (Atlas Obscura, May 18, 2013), https://www.atlasobscura.com/places/cosmonaut-grove.

3. Alan Murphy, "The Losing Hand: Tradition and Superstition in Spaceflight," The Space Review, May 27, 2008, https://www.thespacereview.com/article/1137/1.

4. Scott Kelly, Endurance: A Year in Space, A Lifetime of Discovery (New York: Alfred A. Knopf, 2017), 101.

5. "Soyuz Rocket Rolled Out to the Launchpad by Train," June 4, 2018, photograph, NASA/Joel Kowsky, https://www.nasa.gov/image-feature/the-soyuz-rocket-is-rolled-by-train-to-the-launch-pad.

6. Kelly, Endurance, 22.

7. Clara Moskowitz, "Space Crew Celebrates Movie-Watching Tradition," Space.com, September 30, 2009, https://www.space.com/7357-space-crew-celebrates-movie-watching-tradition.html.

8. Tim Peake, Ask an Astronaut: My Guide to Life in Space (Little Brown and Company, 2017), 19.

9. Peake, Ask an Astronaut, 19.

10. Kelly, Endurance, 24.

11. "Zemlyane - Трава у Дома (Trava u Doma) Lyrics + English Translation (Version #2)," trans. @Firey-Flamy, LyricsTransl.ate.com, accessed May 30, 2021, https://lyricstranslate.com/en/trava-u-doma-%D1%82%D1%80%D0%B0%D0%B2%D0%B0-%D1%83-%D0%B4%D0%BE%D0%BC%D0%B0-grass-home.html.

12. "Gagarin's Traditions," ESA (European Space Agency), accessed May 30, 2021, http://www.esa.int:80/About_Us/ESA_history/50_years_of_humans_in_space/Gagarin_s_traditions.

13. Kelly, Endurance, 25.

14. ESA, "Gagarin's Traditions."

15. Peake, Ask an Astronaut, 11.

16. Peake, Ask an Astronaut, 10

17. Samantha Cristoforetti, Diary of an Apprentice Astronaut, trans. Jill Foulston (Penguin, 2020), 234, Kindle.

18. Peake, Ask an Astronaut, 17.

19. Murphy, "The Losing Hand."

20. Col. Doug Hurley (@Astro_Doug), "Steak and Eggs. Question Answered! Pic.twitter.com/GktFUk9mBK," Twitter (Twitter, May 27, 2020), https://twitter.com/Astro_Doug/status/1265661081873195008?s=20.

21. Find all of NASA's crew posters at: Brian Dunbar, "Space Flight Awareness Posters," ed. Kelli Mars, NASA (NASA, November 2, 2020), https://www.nasa.gov/directorates/heo/sfa/sfa-posters.

22. Tariq Malik, "Sci-Fi to Snoopy: NASA's Coolest Mission Posters (Photos)," Space.com, February 12, 2015, https://www.space.com/26-snoopy-sci-fi-nasa-offbeat-posters.html.

23. NASA, "Expedition 16 Crew Matrix Poster," September 2007, https://www.nasa.gov/pdf/630994main_NW-2007-09-012-JSC%20exp16-themed.pdf.

24. NASA, "Expedition 42 Crew Guide to the Galaxy Poster," July 2014, https://www.nasa.gov/sites/default/files/exp42_sfa_posternw-2014-07-007_highres.pdf

25. NASA, "Expedition 45 Crew Star Wars Poster," January 2015, https://www.nasa.gov/sites/default/files/atoms/files/exp_45_sfa_crew_poster_hi.pdf

26. NASA, "Expedition 30 Crew Pirates Poster," August 2011, https://www.nasa.gov/pdf/630605main_NW-2011-08-012-JSCExp30PosterASTRONAUT%20OFFICE%20CHANGES.pdf

27. NASA, "Expedition 16 Crew Matrix Poster."

28. Elizabeth Howell, "Why Astronauts on SpaceX Rockets Ride a Tesla to the Launchpad," Forbes.com, April 19, 2021, https://www.forbes.com/sites/elizabethhowell1/2021/04/19/why-astronauts-on-spacex-rockets-ride-a-tesla-to-the-launch-pad/?sh=78b597d26d6b.

29. Terry Virts, *How to Astronaut: An Insider's Guide to Leaving Planet Earth* (New York, Workman Publishing, 2020), 69.

30. Virts, *How to Astronaut*, 69.

31. Chris Hadfield, "Rockets: What It Feels Like to Launch," MasterClass (MasterClass), accessed May 30, 2021, https://www.masterclass.com/classes/chris-hadfield-teaches-space-exploration/chapters/rockets-what-it-feels-like-to-launch.

32. "From Trees to Tags, NASA Astronauts Start Traditions before First SpaceX Launch," collectSPACE.com, May 21, 2020, http://www.collectspace.com/news/news-052120a-spacex-demo2-astronauts-traditions.html.

33. Dr. David R. Williams, "Ranger to the Moon (1961 - 1965)," NASA (NASA, last modified September 22, 2005), https://nssdc.gsfc.nasa.gov/planetary/lunar/ranger.html.

34. Tanya Lewis, "Peanuts, Blackjack and Pee: Strangest Space Mission Superstitions," Wired (Conde Nast, September 12, 2018), https://www.wired.com/2012/08/space-mission-superstitions/.

35. Owen Edwards, "Gene Kranz's Apollo Vest," Smithsonian.com (Smithsonian Institution, April 1, 2010), https://www.smithsonianmag.com/history/gene-kranzs-apollo-vest-9045125/.

36. Find the entire Spaceport News issue here: https://www.nasa.gov/centers/kennedy/pdf/67236main_apr12.pdf

37. Marcia Dunn, "NASA Astronaut Welcomed to Mir with Bread, Salt, Bear Hugs," AP NEWS (Associated Press, March 16, 1995), https://apnews.com/article/3e19ef03616e41608230978fef0f7ffd.

38. Kelly, *Endurance*, 10.

39. Brian Dunbar, "2010 Interview: Bill Shepherd," ed. Amiko Kauderer, NASA (NASA, October 27, 2010), https://www.nasa.gov/mission_pages/station/expeditions/shepherd_interview.html.

40. "Key to the International Space Station," collectSPACE, accessed May 30, 2021, http://www.collectspace.com/ubb/Forum14/HTML/001738.html.

41. Cristoforetti, *Diary of an Apprentice Astronaut*, 318.

42. Dunbar, "Bill Shepherd."

43. "Visit the International Space Station," Google Earth.

44. "Visit the International Space Station," Google Earth, accessed May 30, 2021, http://bit.ly/google-earth-iss.

45. Anne Quito, "The Bread That Welcomed NASA Astronaut Scott Kelly Back on Earth," Quartz (Quartz, March 2, 2016), https://qz.com/629502/the-bread-that-welcomed-nasa-astronaut-scott-kelly-back-on-earth/.

46. Jeffrey Kluger, "Scott Kelly Year in Space Comes to an End as Soyuz Lands," Time (Time, March 2, 2016), https://time.com/4244421/scott-kelly-year-in-space-land-soyuz/.

47. Hanneke Weitering, "Amazing Photos: Expedition 54 Crew Returns from the International Space Station," Space.com, March 2, 2018, https://www.space.com/39851-amazing-photos-of-expedition-54-soyuz-landing.html.

48. Weitering, "Expedition 54 Crew Returns."

49. Paul Rincon, "Astronaut Twin Scott Kelly Returns after Year in Space," BBC News (BBC, March 2, 2016), https://www.bbc.co.uk/news/science-environment-35651665.

3, 2, 1 LIFTOFF – FACTS ABOUT LAUNCH

So How Fast Were You Going?

EXCEEDING THE SPEED OF SOUND

In less than a minute, spacecraft go from a standstill to faster than the speed of sound. The rocket reaches its top speed of 17,500 mph (28,000 kph) in about 8 minutes and 40 seconds. That's about 5 miles per second (8 kilometers per second)! That's equivalent to flying from London to Edinburgh in under 90 seconds, or flying from Los Angeles to New York in 8 minutes and 15 seconds!

HOW MANY G'S?

The amount of g-force astronauts experience depends on the spacecraft they travel in. Humans normally experience 1 g at sea level. The space shuttle crews typically experienced 3 g's, which is 3 times the force of gravity during launch and re-entry. Soyuz crews experience forces up to 4.5 g's during launch.[1]

Things don't always go as planned. There have been times when crews have experienced up to 8 g's, like when Peggy Whitson and her crew survived their ballistic Soyuz re-entry in 2008[2] or the 7 g's experienced when the emergency escape system was triggered on the Soyuz in October 2018.[3]

ALAN SHEPARD'S SPEEDY JOURNEY

On the Soyuz, it takes a little over three minutes to reach space—which officially is defined as 62 miles (100 km). Alan Shepard, the first American in space, launched on a Mercury-Redstone rocket that was derived from a U.S. Army ballistic missile. His journey into space was a speedy one. Shepard reached 177 miles (188 km) in about 2.5 minutes and experienced 6.3 g on the way up![4]

WHERE SPACE STARTS: THE KÁRMÁN LINE

According to the International Astronautical Federation, space begins at 62 miles (100 km) above sea level, at the Kármán line. The Kármán line is named after Hungarian physicist Theodore von Kármán, who determined the space boundary in the 1900s.[5] In case you were wondering, it takes a little over three minutes to get there in Russia's Soyuz.[6]

AUDIO COMMENTARY IN THE SOYUZ

When flying onboard the Soyuz, it's a sacred custom for the crew to report everything by radio, even though the Russian TsUP (Mission Control) controllers can see everything the crew can see. This habit may harken back to a time when video transmission was less reliable.[7]

Becoming Weightless

IT'S COMMON TO LAUGH

After the engines shut off and astronauts have escaped Earth's gravity, hair starts to float and other items around them float by. This is an out-of-this-world experience, for which laughter is the most common response. The astronauts just survived a very dangerous thing by launching into space on top of a rocket. Laughing is also a way of releasing a huge sense of relief of getting to where they are.[8]

IT FLOATS!

The mission's commander gets to choose the mission mascot, or talisman. This is usually a small cuddly toy that hangs from the instrument panel. The mascot will be the first object to float once they reach orbit, letting the crew know they are now weightless.

Some examples of past mascots include a cute toy giraffe that belonged to NASA astronaut Reid Wiseman's daughter. More recently a sparkly dragon, Baby Yoda and a penguin toy named Guin Guin[9] have been the mascots in the SpaceX Dragon capsules. Olaf from *Frozen* was the mascot for Samantha Cristoforetti's Soyuz launch.[10]

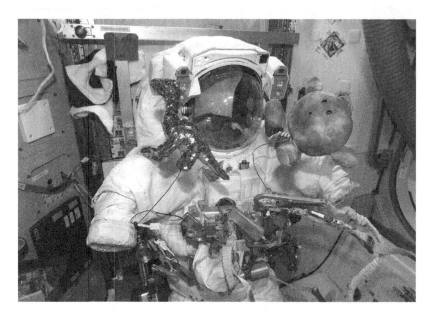

Tremor the dinosaur and Little Earth were two of the plush-doll mascots that flew onboard the first two SpaceX Crew Dragon vehicles. Photo courtesy of NASA.

NOSEPRINTS ON THE SPACESHIP WINDOWS

One of the first things astronauts do after completing critical items on their checklists, is unstrap themselves, clumsily float over to a window and enjoy the magnificent view of our world. Often their noses will press up against the window and leave a smudge because they don't yet know how to control themselves in microgravity.[11]

In Case a Launch Goes Wrong

TERMINAL COUNTDOWN DEMONSTRATION TEST

During the space shuttle program, astronauts were trained to deal with any emergency while the shuttle was still on the launchpad. Part of that training included escaping the orbiter unassisted, crossing the platform and climbing into four refrigerator-sized wire-mesh baskets at the top of launchpad. Astronauts would crawl into them two by two with their visors down and locked. They also activated their emergency oxygen bottles. Once inside the basket, the astronauts would release the basket and it would slide down a wire several hundred feet to the ground then safely slow to a halt and land in a big pit of sand.

The astronauts would then rush to an armored personnel carrier and drive it to a safehouse, which was an underground bunker about a mile away. There they would wait for further instructions.[12]

THE RED BUTTON IN LAUNCH CONTROL

There was a red button in launch control that was to be used in the extremely unlikely event that the space shuttle, or even an unmanned rocket, veered off course and headed toward Disney World in Orlando or other populated areas. This was part of the Flight Termination System (FTS).

The red button was only to be used as a last resort. Before the red button was pressed, there were several steps to take. If a problem started within the first 90 seconds of launch, backup computers would engage to hopefully fix the trajectory. If the problem started after 90 seconds, the crew commander could take over and manually steer the shuttle out to sea, away from populated areas.

If both of those options failed, Houston would call the crew with a secret code word that would warn them of what was about to happen. Then the Range Safety Officer would press the red button. This would trigger multiple radio-detonated explosive devices on the solid rocket boosters and external tank, which would cause the rocket to split apart before reaching populated areas. This meant that the astronauts onboard would be killed in order to save thousands of citizens.

The space shuttle itself didn't have any self-destruct devices, but the solid rocket boosters and external tank both did.

While the Flight Termination System was used to terminate unmanned rockets that went off course, it was never used to terminate a crewed mission.[13]

CHALLENGER'S SOLID ROCKET BOOSTERS

On January 28, 1986, after the *Challenger* space shuttle broke apart in flight and the external tank was destroyed, the Solid Rocket Boosters (SRB) broke away and continued to fly and to stabilize. The Range Safety Officer at the Cape Canaveral Air Force Station felt the boosters might endanger land or shipping areas. The command to ARM and FIRE the range safety explosive package on the SRB were sent, and 110 seconds after launch, they were destroyed.[14]

DID YOU KNOW?

Every major vehicle flown from the Cape Canaveral area has carried an explosive destruct system that could be armed and fired by the Range Safety Officer to prevent loss of life and property that could result from a vehicle or its components falling into populated areas.[15]

NOTES

1. Brian Dunbar, "The Soyuz Flight to ISS…," ed. Amiko Kauderer, NASA (NASA, October 23, 2010), https://www.nasa.gov/mission_pages/station/expeditions/expedition13/journals_williams_1.html.

2. Denise Chow, "Soyuz Astronauts' Emergency Descent Was a Harrowing, High-G Ordeal," NBCNews.com (NBCUniversal News Group, October 11, 2018), https://www.nbcnews.com/mach/science/astronauts-emergency-descent-was-harrowing-high-g-ordeal-ncna919246.

3. Hanneke Weitering, "Astronaut, Cosmonaut in 'Good Health' After Surviving Soyuz Rocket Launch Failure," Space.com, October 11, 2018, https://www.space.com/42109-soyuz-launch-failure-astronaut-crew-good-health.html.

4. Tim Peake, *Ask an Astronaut: My Guide to Life in Space* (Little Brown and Company, 2017), 33.

5. Nadia Drake, "Where, exactly, is the edge of space? It depends on who you ask," NationalGeographic.com, December 20, 2018, https://www.nationalgeographic.com/science/article/where-is-the-edge-of-space-and-what-is-the-karman-line?loggedin=true.

6. Peake, *Ask an Astronaut*, 32.

7.   Samantha Cristoforetti, *Diary of an Apprentice Astronaut*, trans. Jill Foulston (Penguin, 2020), 245, Kindle.

8.   Chris Hadfield, "Spacewalking: Space and Perspective," MasterClass (MasterClass), accessed May 30, 2021, https://www.masterclass.com/classes/chris-hadfield-teaches-space-exploration/chapters/spacewalking-space-and-perspective.

9.   Aylin Woodward, "SpaceX's New Astronaut Crew Brought a Cute, Fluffy Penguin Toy Named 'Guin Guin' into Orbit," Business Insider (Business Insider, April 23, 2021), https://www.businessinsider.com/spacex-crew-2-astronauts-fluffy-penguin-toy-orbit-2021-4.

10. Cristoforetti, *Diary of an Apprentice Astronaut*, 230.

11. Hadfield, "Spacewalking."

12. Terry Virts, *How to Astronaut: An Insider's Guide to Leaving Planet Earth* (New York, Workman Publishing, 2020), 65-66.

13. Virts, *How to Astronaut*, 73-74.

14. "Chapter IX: Other Safety Considerations," Report of the PRESIDENTIAL COMMISSION on the Space Shuttle Challenger Accident (NASA), accessed May 30, 2021, https://history.nasa.gov/rogersrep/v1ch9.htm.

15. NASA, "Other Safety Considerations."

SPACESUITS VS PRESSURE SUITS

Astronauts wear both spacesuits and pressure suits. Each serves a very different purpose. Spacesuits are worn outside of the spacecraft when performing spacewalks, aka EVAs. Spacesuits are basically individual spacecraft, since it is built with everything—from breathing units to radiation shields—to keep the astronaut alive while in space.

During launch and landing, astronauts wear pressure suits. These are built to maintain a safe air pressure for the astronaut in case their space vehicle loses pressure during launch or re-entry.

Russian Cosmonaut Outfits

SK SERIES (1961-1963)

SK stands for Skafandr Kosmicheskiy, which means "space suit" or "diving suit for space" in Russian. SK suits were designed to allow cosmonauts to eject and land separately from the Vostok spacecraft. SK-1 was the suit designed specifically for Yuri Gagarin and was the first spacesuit ever used. The SK-2 suit was exactly the same as SK-1, except that it was designed for the first woman in space, Valentina Tereshkova. The suit weighed 44 lbs. (20 kg).

RUSSIA'S BERKUT EVA SUIT (1965)

Berkut means "golden eagle" in Russian. This was the suit used for the first spacewalk by cosmonaut Alexey Leonov. During his 12 minute, 9 second EVA, Leonov's suit ballooned and stiffened to the point where he could no longer pull himself back into his spacecraft. He was able to depressurize the suit to the point at which he could get into the airlock and pull it shut. The Berkut was only used during this one mission. It included a 45-minute life-support backpack and weighed 90 lbs. (41 kg).

NASA *astronaut Michael Fincke in his Russian Sokol flight suit, in the* International Space Station. Photo courtesy of NASA.[1]

SOKOL LAUNCH AND ENTRY SUIT (1973-PRESENT)

Russia's equivalent to NASA's orange launch suit is the blue-lined spacesuit called the Sokol suit. Sokol means "falcon" in Russian. Every Sokol suit is custom made for every cosmonaut or astronaut flying in the Soyuz. It takes one year and 70 different measurements to sew the custom Sokol suits for each cosmonaut.[2]

The Sokol is a pressurized suit that weighs 22 lbs. (10 kg). Interestingly, the pressure seal is made by two rubber bands that are wrapped around the main opening. Even though these suits are custom made and are comfortable while sitting down, they aren't designed for walking. This is why you'll see the "cosmonaut stoop,"[3] which is the hunched-over pose cosmonauts have as they walk from the bus to the Soyuz launchpad.[4]

Russian cosmonaut Oleg Kotov, Expedition 22 flight engineer, works with a Russian Orlan spacesuit in the Pirs Docking Compartment of the International Space Station. Photo courtesy of NASA.[5]

ORLAN SPACESUIT (1977-PRESENT)

Cosmonauts use the Orlan spacesuit during spacewalks, or EVAs. It's similar to NASA's EMU (Extravehicular Mobility Unit.) Orlan is the Russian word for "sea eagle."

The current Orlan suit used onboard the ISS is the Orlan MKS model, which weighs 130 lbs. (59 kg). The Orlan suit isn't just used by Russian cosmonauts. It's been used by American, European, Canadian and Chinese astronauts, too.

The MKS acronym stands for "modernized" "komputerized" and "synthetic." The new model includes a computerized climate-control system to help regulate suit temperature, has a built-in computer with a larger color display screen to make it easier to read, and synthetic material that is easier to manufacture, but with improved toughness to stand up to wear and tear.[6]

EASY TO GET INTO

The Orlan suit isn't something you "put on." It's a one-piece suit you get inside of. You enter through the back of the suit in a rear hatch on the life-support backpack. It only takes 5 minutes to suit up in the Orlan, whereas it takes 45 minutes for NASA's EMU. Cosmonauts can put their own Orlan spacesuits on without help, unlike the EMU.

ONE SIZE FITS MOST

The Orlan suit only comes in one size which means it's bulkier and harder to move around in. The tallest acceptable height for using the Orlan is 6 feet, 2 inches (190 cm). The shortest acceptable height is 5 feet, 4 inches (165 cm).[7] The Orlan can be adjusted at the arms, legs and pelvis by pulling on different cords that bunch up or pleat the fabric.[8]

STIFF AND HARD TO MOVE IN

The Orlan suit operates at a pressure of 5.8 psi, which makes the suit stiff and hard to move around in. However, the higher pressure does make it less likely that the cosmonaut wearing it will get the bends, which is decompression sickness.

ORLAN GLOVES

The Orlan is a one-piece suit except for the gloves, which attach separately. The gloves come in three different sizes, but the only difference is in finger length. Unlike the EMU gloves, the Orlan gloves don't allow for cosmonauts to wear any sort of padding inside to protect their hands.[9]

ORLAN HELMET

The helmet is attached to the suit and offers a much wider field of view than the EMU helmet. It's roomy and includes a little window on the top that makes it possible to see above you![10]

CHINA'S FEITIAN SPACESUIT

China's EVA spacesuit is modeled after Russia's Orlan suit. The name Feitian comes from the words means "flying" and "sky" in Mandarin. It also references the spirit called the "flying deva" in Buddhism. These massive suits weigh 260 lbs. (120 kg) and can be used on spacewalks for up to seven hours. The first Chinese "space rambler" to use the Feitian spacesuit and the first to spacewalk was 42-year-old Zhai Zhigang in September of 2008.[11]

NASA's Gear

MERCURY LAUNCH SUIT (1961-1963)

NASA's first spacesuit was a modified high-altitude jet aircraft pressure suit. The first six American astronauts wore these into space before they were retired and newer suits were designed.[12]

THE FIRST SPACESUIT WAS PEED IN

Alan Shepard, the first American in space, was only supposed to be in his suit for 5 hours and only in space for 15 minutes. Spacesuit engineers didn't expect that he would need to go to the bathroom during that time and didn't design a way for him to do just that.[13]

Due to delays on the launchpad, he ended up being in his suit for 8 hours and developed the urgent need to relieve himself. Shepard was told to pee in his suit, so he did. But he ended up short circuiting his heart and respiration monitors in the process. Every astronaut since has been equipped with some sort of urine collection device or absorbent garment (aka adult diaper!).[14]

GEMINI LAUNCH SUIT (1965-1966)

With feedback from the Mercury astronauts, NASA designed the Gemini suit to be more comfortable. One of the most exciting features was that it came with an air conditioner to help keep the astronaut cool. These suits weighed 16 to 34 lbs. (7.25 to 15.4 kg).

*Astronaut Gordon Cooper
in the Mercury spacesuit.
Photo courtesy of NASA.*[15]

GEMINI SPACEWALK SUIT (1967-1975)

These were the first suits NASA designed for astronauts to spacewalk in. They had a hose that connected the astronaut to the spacecraft and provided oxygen. In case of an emergency, the suit also had 30 minutes of backup life support. One version of this suit weighed about 34 lbs. (15.4 kg).

Buzz Aldrin on the surface of the Moon wearing his custom-made Apollo spacesuit. Photo by Neil Armstrong. Photo courtesy of NASA.[16]

APOLLO SPACEWALK SUIT (1967-1975)

Dressing for the Moon was a unique challenge. These suits had to be flexible enough to allow astronauts to bend down and collect Moon rocks, but also had to be tough enough to protect from the Moon dust that was as sharp as glass. Intense changes in temperature also meant that the suit had to withstand the extreme heat from the sun and keep the astronaut warm during the bitter cold that came when the sun disappeared. These suits also needed to provide several hours of life support while the astronauts were away from their Lunar Modules.

Each Apollo spacesuit was custom-made to fit each astronaut and were basically one-piece suits. To put on the suit, astronauts entered from the back. [17]

Every astronaut that went to the Moon had 3 custom-made spacesuits: one for the flight, one for training, and one as backup.

These suits weighed 180 lbs. (81.6 kg) on Earth, but only 1/6 of that in Moon's gravity. This means it felt like only 30 lbs. (13.6 kg) while walking on the Moon.

THE FIRST SPACE SHUTTLE SUITS (1982-1986)

All astronauts on space shuttle flights STS-5 through STS-51-L (the *Challenger* disaster) wore a one-piece light blue flight suit with escape harnesses and a motorcycle-like helmet for launch, like they would if they were flying jets.

After the *Challenger* disaster, it became clear that some launch and landing accidents could be survivable if the crews wore pressure suits. Astronauts went back to wearing pressure suits that were modeled after the U-2 spy plane suit. The first version was called Launch Entry Suits, or LES.[18]

SPACE SHUTTLE FLIGHT SUITS 2.0 (1988-1994)

These LES suits were nicknamed "pumpkin suits" because of their orange color. These early suits were partial pressure suits and were modeled after the U-2 spy plane suit.

ACES SUITS (1988-2011)

The next version of the suits were also nicknamed pumpkin suits for their bright-orange hue. They were called ACES suits, which stands for Advanced Crew Escape System, and were worn during launch and re-entry. ACES were full pressure suits. The orange color was so that it would be easier for rescue teams to spot the astronauts in the dark blue ocean in case they had to a bailout during launch or re-entry. These suits also included gloves, an extra layer of insulation, liquid cooling and improved ventilation. They had a detachable helmet and a survival backpack. These are similar to Russia's Sokol suit except that the Sokol suit has an integrated helmet and no backpack.

STARMAN SUIT (2019-PRESENT)

To make SpaceX's signature suit, Elon Musk teamed up with the Hollywood designer, Jose Fernandez, who has designed superhero costumes for *Wonder Woman*, *Wolverine*, and *Captain America: Civil War*. Fernandez also knows a thing or two about designing helmets. He designed the helmets for Loki and Thor in the movie *Thor*. These custom-made, one-piece, slim cut, non-bulky, flexible and

"Pumpkin Suits" also known as Advanced Crew Escape System or ACES suit. Photo courtesy of NASA.[19]

pressurized spacesuits resemble a tuxedo. And everyone looks better in a tuxedo—especially while launching into space! The additional custom-made high boots just add to the super-hero look [20]

NASA doesn't require that all launch suits need to be orange, so SpaceX went with white and dark gray. The white suits are made of Teflon, which makes them flame- and water-resistant. One umbilical cable provides oxygen, and their communication link from the

SpaceX Spacesuit. Photo courtesy of NASA and SpaceX. [21]

connection point on their right thigh plugs into their seat on the Crew Dragon capsule.[22]

3D PRINTED HELMETS
Helmets are built into the suit and are 3D-printed. Each helmet includes integrated valves, microphones and speakers. Wearers can also retract and lock the visor.[23]

SUIT GLOVES
Gloves are some of the most important parts of a spacesuit, whether it's a launch suit or an EVA suit. The SpaceX gloves are no different.

These are designed to work with the touch screen controls found inside the Crew Dragon capsule. Unlike other spacecraft, the Crew Dragon control panel is touchscreen only.[24]

NASA'S EXTRAVEHICULAR MOBILITY UNITS (1983-PRESENT)

Extravehicular Mobility Units, or EMUs, are suits that are essentially solo spaceships. They include everything the astronaut needs to stay alive and comfortable while out in open space away from the International Space Station. These suits are equivalent to Russia's Orlan suit. The shuttle EMU weighed about 275 lbs. (124.7 kg). The newer ISS EMU weighs approximately 319 lbs. (145 kg). They protect the wearer from the sun's intense radiation, extreme changes in temperature and tiny meteorites flying at orbital speeds. They also provide the oxygen needed for up to seven hours while spacewalking. They provide enough range of motion so that an astronaut can perform necessary work, like using tools to make repairs on the ISS during their EVAs.

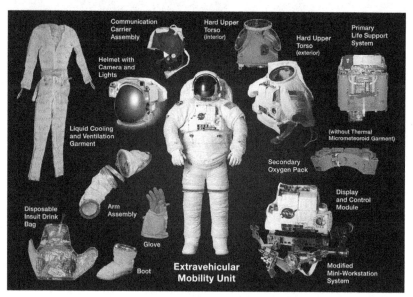

Part of NASA's Extravehicular Mobility Unit (EMU) spacesuit. Photo courtesy of NASA.[25]

UNDER PRESSURE

Unlike the Russian Orlan suits, which operate at a pressure of 5.8 psi, EMUs have an operating pressure of 4.3 psi, which is equal to one-third of an atmosphere. This is lower than the pressure at the summit of Mt. Everest, which is 4.89 psi. The low pressure allows the astronaut to move around in the suit more easily, but it's just above the limit where dissolved nitrogen in the body can start to form tiny bubbles and cause the bends, or decompression sickness.

To decrease the risk of getting the bends, astronauts flush as much nitrogen out of the body as possible before their spacewalk. They breathe 100% oxygen, and depressurize the airlock to 10.2 psi while getting dressed for their EVA. Doing light exercises for 50 minutes while in the suit at this pressure helps reduce their risk. They also breathe 100% oxygen during their spacewalks, which also helps.

NASA decided to make this trade-off because astronauts spend several hours on spacewalks. Designing the spacesuit so it's as easy to maneuver as possible makes a huge difference. It reduces the effort it takes to do even the smallest tasks.

THE AIR INSIDE THE SUIT

Because the pressure is so low, it's important to get as much oxygen as possible into the suit for breathing. Instead of a mix of air, astronauts breathe 100% oxygen while in the spacesuit.

PORTABLE LIFE SUPPORT SYSTEM

The PLSS (Portable Life Support System) backpack that is attached to the back of the EVA suit is the main life-support system. It has an oxygen purification system, battery power, a radio and a cooling system. It's the "nuts and bolts" of the suit that is keeping the astronaut alive.

SUIT CAMERAS

At the top of the EMU suit, there is a camera that allows ground support to be an extra set of eyes. A button can be pressed by the astronaut that turns it on. It can also be pressed multiple times to change camera lenses. This allows Mission Control to get a recorded visual record of the spacewalk.

SPACESUIT LIGHTS

Powerful lights at the top of the suit allow the astronauts to continue to work when the sun starts to go down or while they are in the shadow of the earth. These lights can then be turned off once the sun rises.

EMU GLOVES

The gloves of a spacesuit are one of the most important pieces of the suit. While it's referred to as spacewalking, astronauts don't actually walk with their feet in space. They push and pull their way along the ISS with their hands. The gloves are also the most fragile part of the suit. To make it as flexible as possible to allow the hands to do what they need to do, the gloves are only one layer of rubber.

MAKING THE GLOVES

The spacesuit gloves are the most challenging part of the suit to design, so NASA uses advanced technology. A laser scanner creates a 3D image of the astronaut's hand. Then a computer creates a pattern specially designed for each hand. Next, glove parts are stitched together using sewing machines—or sometimes by hand—to make sure it's perfect. To create the inner bladder of the glove, a 3D printer prints a physical model of the astronaut's hand.

After the gloves are made, they go through rigorous testing and inspections to make sure they won't fail in space. Leak checks are especially important.[26]

GLOVE HEATERS

The rest of the EVA suit has 14 different layers to protect the wearer, but the gloves are only one layer thick. This means an astronaut's hands get cold more easily than the rest of their body. To help, the EMU gloves have battery-powered heaters in them. To turn the glove heaters on, the astronaut grabs and pulls a cloth tab on the back of the gloves.[27]

GLOVE LINERS AND MOLESKIN PATCHES

Not only do the hands get cold, but hands and fingers take a beating during spacewalks. Astronauts will often attach moleskin patches to their fingers and then wear a glove liner over the top for added comfort, protection and warmth.

TWO PAIRS OF GLOVES

If you've ever lost a glove when you needed it, you'll understand the importance of having a backup pair! Every astronaut and cosmonaut has two pairs of gloves while in space in case one gets damaged during a spacewalk or ends up not fitting if their fingers swell.[28] While other backup parts of the suit stay on the ISS, the gloves travel with the astronaut or cosmonaut.

INSPECTING THE GLOVES

At every sunrise and sunset, astronauts will inspect their gloves carefully for any leaks that may have developed while out on their spacewalks. They need to make sure they haven't snagged the gloves or worn through them.

PALM BAR

To prevent material from bunching up in the palm, a metal bar is placed across an astronaut's palm. On the back of the glove there is a Velcro strap. If pulled tight, that strap pulls the bar and any loose material back to prevent bunching. It's common to see astronauts pull on that Velcro strap to cinch up the palm bar right before, or during, spacewalks.

EMU HELMET

Unlike Russian's Orlan suit, NASA's EMU helmet is detachable. It has several different features that protects the astronaut from heat and the sun's radiation, keeps oxygen flowing, allows the wearer to equalize their ears and scratch their nose and even includes a drinking straw and a snorkel.

SCRATCH YOUR NOSE AND EQUALIZE YOUR EARS

Having an itch you can't scratch is almost unbearable. Having an itchy nose while on a spacewalk could make it difficult to focus on the important tasks at hand. Helmets come equipped with a Valsalva device, that does the same thing as holding your nose. This small piece of soft rubber is glued to the base of the helmet and is used to equalize your ears by pressing the base of your nostrils against it to seal them and then gently blowing.[29]

This same device can also be used to itch your nose. Some astronauts have also attached a small piece of Velcro inside their helmet to scratch that itchy nose!

BULLET-PROOF VISORS

The spacesuit helmet includes two layers of visors. One is tinted and one is clear. Both are made with the material used in bullet-proof glass. This helps protect the astronaut from micrometeorites.[30]

GOLD VISOR

To protect the astronauts from radiation when working in the sun, a very thin and see-through gold visor can be slid down over the front of the helmet. It's only about 50 cents worth of pounded gold. But this thin layer is all they need for protection.

HELMET "BALL CAP"

The helmet has a protective shield that allows you to slide it partway down the visor. This blocks the sun in way that is similar to how the stiff brim on the front of a ball cap does.

SIDE SUN SHIELD

In case you need to block the sun on the side of your face, there are side sun blockers that also can be slid down the side of the helmet.

HELMET PURGE VALVE

In case you need to purge the air from the suit, there's a purge valve on the side of the helmet. Astronaut Chris Hadfield became blinded by contaminated air in his suit and had to purge some of the air from his suit so he could see again.[31]

HELMET DIAPER & SNORKEL

After a clogged filter caused water to build up in Italian astronaut Luca Parmitano's helmet during a spacewalk—and made drowning a real possibility—changes were made to prevent this from ever happening again.

EMU Helmets now include a large absorbent pad that is worn behind the astronaut's heads. The pad soaks up any water that might leak into the helmet. In case there's too much water for the pad, a snorkel inside the helmet makes it possible to breathe air from a separate part of the suit in the chest region.[32]

PREVENTING HELMET FOGGING

Two things help prevent an astronaut's helmet from fogging up during a spacewalk. First, the helmet has a vent that directs clean dry air up over the astronaut's head and across the front of the visor. Second, astronauts can use disposable antifog wipes on the visor, like the kind you find at automotive parts stores for your car's windshield.[33]

VISION CORRECTION LENS

Some astronauts wear glasses in space. But wearing glasses during a spacewalk isn't ideal since glasses can slip and there's no way to adjust them while wearing a spacesuit. For astronauts who can't wear contacts, they have had their spacesuit helmet visors fitted with special lenses to correct their vision without having to wear glasses.[34]

DISPLAY AND CONTROL MODULE

On top of the display and control module, the astronaut can glance down and see a variety of things. There is little computer screen, another purge valve, pressure gauge, radio controls and fans that can be turned on or off. Little alarms inside the helmet will go off to prompt the astronaut to look down at the computer screen to see things like how much battery power and oxygen are left.

THERMOSTAT

On the front of the suit is an easy-to-turn thermostat to adjust how warm or cool the suit is. The astronauts use the mirror on their wrist to see the thermostat, and then use the other hand to adjust it. The lettering on the thermostat and at other places on the suit are written backwards so that it can be read correctly when viewing it from their wrist mirrors.

VOLUME AND BRIGHTNESS CONTROLS

Also on the front of the suit, just under the Display and Control Module, there are controls to adjust the volume of the headset the astronaut is wearing and the brightness of the computer screen.

WHY A WHITE SUIT?

The EVA suits used by both NASA and Russia's Roscosmos space agency are white because they reflect the heat of the sun. White also makes it easy to spot the spacewalking astronauts against the blackness of space.[35]

LOOK FOR THE RED STRIPE

Back when Neil Armstrong and Buzz Aldrin made their historic visit to the Moon, the folks sifting through the photos once they got back realized that they couldn't tell who was who. The suits were exactly the same and there was no way to differentiate between the two. They learned this the hard way when they were trying to find a photograph of Neil Armstrong. It turns out there is only one photograph of him, since Armstrong was taking most of the photos and wasn't really into selfies!

Since then, red or yellow stripes have been added to the EVA suits so it's obvious who is who. NASA astronauts will have a lead spacewalker who is in charge of the spacewalk. To distinguish which astronaut is the lead spacewalker, look for the color of the stripes that are found on the arms and legs of the suit and on the back of the backpack.

The astronaut wearing the red stripe is normally the lead EVA astronaut.

SPACE BOOTS

While astronauts don't really use their feet during spacewalks, it's still important that the boots are comfortable. Often their feet tend to get in the way. The boots have a special pattern on them that allows the boots to fit under toe loops found on different parts of the outside of the station. This enables the spacewalker to lock their feet into what's called a Portable Foot Restraint, or PFR.

Spacesuit Accessories

SPACE TOOL BELT

Astronauts have a mini utility workstation that clips into the front of the suit that allows them to attach all of the different space tools they'll need while out on their spacewalk. It's like Batman's utility belt...but for space!

SAFETY TETHER & METAL LINKS

The only link from the suit to the space station is a tiny cable sides. It clips onto two metal links that are found on the left and right side of the suit below the space tool belt. So, if an astronaut loses their grip and "falls" off the station, they are able to reel themselves in on this cable and won't be lost in space.

CABLE REEL

The safety tether is about 60 feet (18 meters) long and is on a reel that allows the astronaut to reel it in to take up the slack. However, the tether also makes it easy for astronauts to let themselves out as they move around the space station.

WRIST MIRRORS

It's not easy to move around while in a spacesuit, and things can be hard to see during a spacewalk. Astronauts wear mirrors attached to their wrist that helps them see what they are doing. The controls on the chest of the suit all have labels that are written backwards so they can be read easily when looking in the mirror.[36]

ESA Astronaut Luca Parmitano wrist mirror during his spacewalk. Photo taken by Luca Parmitano. Photo courtesy of ESA and NASA. [37]

EMERGENCY CUFF CHECKLIST

While out on their spacewalks, astronauts wear a small spiral-bound emergency checklist with 40 stiff pages on the forearm. This way critical information is within reach and easy to flip through.[38]

NASA APPROVED EVA WATCHES

Tracking time during an EVA is critical. Having a reliable watch, or more specifically a chronograph that works in the vacuum of space, is important. The watch needs to be waterproof, shockproof, anti-magnetic, have loud alarms that can be heard over background noise and be able to withstand intense temperatures. Only the Omega Speedmaster chronograph met all of those requirements. Omega Speedmaster watches were worn for all of the Gemini and Apollo EVAs.

Today, NASA and the European Space Agency (ESA) still work with Omega to design a watch for living and working in space. The Omega Speedmaster X-33 Skywalker watch was developed for astronauts living and working on the ISS. One of the key features is multiple alarms that can be heard over the ever-present background noise of the ISS.

ASTRONAUTS CAN WEAR OTHER WATCHES

Like everything else that makes it to the ISS, watches must pass NASA's safety requirements. If astronauts want to wear something other than the Omega watch, there are a few more requirements: Certain batteries aren't allowed because not all batteries are built to withstand the extreme temperatures of the space environment and some batteries are known to overheat and explode, and the watch face needs to be made from a shatterproof material like hesalite crystal.[39]

THE ASTRONAUT JETPACK

Strapped to the back of the Life Support System Pack is a jetpack called SAFER, which stands for Simplified Aid for EVA Rescue. SAFER is activated by pulling on a handle. If necessary, a joystick pops out of the right side of the backpack. Then, the astronaut can use the joystick to control 24 tiny thrusters that blow out puffs of nitrogen

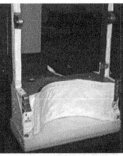

Astronaut Mark Lee testing the SAFER jetpack while floating tether-free. SAFER jetpack components. Image montage by the author. Photos courtesy of NASA. [40] [41]

gas. These puffs of nitrogen help an astronaut stabilize themselves in space, and hopefully make it back to the station before running out of the nitrogen. It's to be used for emergencies only.

THE MMU

Before there was the SAFER jetpack, there was the MMU, the Manned Maneuvering Unit. It was used to perform untethered EVAs during three shuttle missions in 1984. But it was retired following a safety review after the *Challenger* disaster. The MMU was classified as an unnecessary risk, since many of the same activities could be carried out by robotic arms or tethered EVAs.

THE JETPACK TEST

Before being qualified to go out and do a spacewalk, astronauts have to pass tests that involve drifting away from the station, using the jetpack to stop yourself from spinning, and navigating back to the station.

LEARNING TO FLY A JETPACK

The Johnson Space Center in Houston has a Virtual Reality Lab with a full-immersive training environment. Astronauts are repeatedly sent tumbling off into "space" so they can learn how to safely get back to the space station. Astronauts practice being thrown off the station 20 to 30 times, simulating both day and night scenarios, before taking a final exam.[42]

Future Spacesuits

ARTEMIS SUITS

A new bright orange launch and re-entry suit will be used for the future Artemis missions to the Moon. They are called Orion Crew Survival System (OCSS) suits. These flight suits have had both design and engineering enhancements from head to toe. They are custom-fit to each astronaut rather than coming in generic small, medium and large sizes like they did during the shuttle era. The suits are pressure

Orion Crew Survival System (OCSS) launch and re-entry suits. Photo courtesy of NASA.[43]

suits, but have been engineered to be more comfortable and easier to move around in. The gloves now are touchscreen compatible, fit better and are much more durable. Even the suit zippers got an upgrade. Now it's much easier to get in and out of the suits quickly.

The suits make it possible for the astronauts to survive up to six days if the spacecraft loses air pressure. The suits are integrated with the seats and both work together with the Orion spacecraft. The suits have an umbilical cord that hooks into the Orion spacecraft, which provides life support systems like oxygen and water for cooling the suit.

The suit also comes with survival gear if they have to exit Orion after a water landing. The suits are bright orange to make them easier to spot against the dark blue ocean. The suits come with built-in life preservers, a personal locator beacon, a rescue knife and a signaling kit that includes a mirror, strobe light, flashlight, whistle and light sticks. The suits are also dry suits, and can help keep them warm in water temperatures down to about 50°F (10°C).[44]

NEW MOONWALK SPACESUITS

NASA is upgrading the suits the Artemis astronauts will use as they explore the Moon in the coming years. The new Exploration Extravehicular Mobility Units (xEMU) suits have been enhanced from head to toe.

The new Exploration Extravehicular Mobility Unit (xEMU) suit that will be used by Artemis astronauts. NASA administrator, Jim Bridenstine, high fives Kristine Davis, a NASA spacesuit engineer during Artemis Generation Spacesuit Event. Photo courtesy of NASA.[45]

ENHANCED MOBILITY

One of the biggest changes had been to make it easier to move around and walk. Instead of the hopping and shuffling Apollo astronauts did before, the xEMU suits will allow astronauts to walk normally. Before, when astronauts had to pick something up from the ground, they had to perform an awkward lunge and then a pushup to get back up. Now, astronauts will be able to just bend down and pick things up off the lunar surface, like we do on Earth.[46]

ENHANCED HELMET

The new xEMU helmet weighs less, comes in multiple sizes and has a much wider range of vision than any other helmet currently used. The Artemis astronauts will be able to look up and see the sky, look down and see their feet, look left and look right. Artemis astronauts will be exploring Moon craters, so the helmets now have lights that will light up darker places.[47]

The new helmets will also have a heads-up display feature that will provide information about the suit to the wearer. In the movie *Iron Man*, character Tony Stark had a suit with a heads-up display, or HUD, that gave him real-time information about the suit. Teams are conducting research to identify what types of information Artemis astronauts will want to see on the display.[48]

HIGH-DEF CAMERAS

High-definition video cameras will be at shoulder level and will allow the rest of us on Earth to see what the Artemis astronauts are seeing while on the Moon.

NEW COMMUNICATION SYSTEMS

The communication system has also been enhanced. Since the early days of the space program, astronauts have worn the Snoopy cap headsets. But these have been known to become sweaty, and the communication systems aren't always reliable. So, the xEMU suits will do away with the Snoopy cap and the communication system will be embedded into the suit and be voice-activated.[49]

CONTINUOUS AIR RECYCLING

The xEMU suits will have a continuous carbon dioxide scrubbing system, with two separate absorption beds. While one bed is being used, the other is exposed to a vacuum, and burns off the CO_2. When the other bed fills up, the system switches. This makes it possible for the astronauts to stay out on a lunar EVA much longer than the Apollo astronauts.

BUILT WITH MARS IN MIND

The suits have been designed to have the same core system that will be used on the ISS, the planned small space station called the Gateway in the lunar orbit, on the Moon and on Mars. They will have interchangeable parts that can adapt to the different environments and situations. These suits will be tested on the ISS before the first trip to the Moon, currently planned to take place in 2024.[50]

BOEING BLUE SPACESUIT

Future passengers on the commercial Boeing CST-100 Starliner spacecraft will wear the Boeing Blue launch and re-entry suits. These pressure suits are about 40% lighter than traditional space flight suits. The lightweight leather gloves are touchscreen-friendly. The helmet is soft and hood-like with a wide visor and zipper closure. The boots, which are breathable and slip-resistant, are made in partnership with Reebok.[51]

VIRGIN GALACTIC SPACESUIT

Virgin Galactic teamed up with Under Armour to design their spacesuits for both pilots and passengers. Each flight participant will have a blue suit custom-tailored to them. The suit will include the wearer's country flag and a name badge. Their spacewear "system" includes a base layer, spacesuit, footwear, training suit and a limited-edition Virgin Galactic astronaut jacket.[52]

NOTES

1. "Sokol IV Spacesuit Prep," March 25, 2009, photograph, NASA, https://images.nasa.gov/details-iss018e043382.

2. Samantha Cristoforetti, *Diary of an Apprentice Astronaut*, trans. Jill Foulston (Penguin, 2020), 135, Kindle.

3. Doug Millard, "11 Things You Might Not Know about Tim Peake's Spacesuit," Science Museum Blog (Science Museum Group, March 9, 2018), https://blog.sciencemuseum.org.uk/11-things-you-might-not-know-about-tim-peakes-spacesuit/.

4. "Luca Parmitano in His Sokol Spacesuit," ESA (European Space Agency, July 20, 2019), https://www.esa.int/ESA_Multimedia/Images/2019/07/Luca_Parmitano_in_his_Sokol_spacesuit2.

5. "Russian Orlan spacesuit," January 11, 2010, photograph, NASA, https://images.nasa.gov/details-iss022e023617.

6. Anatoly Zak, "Orlan MKS Spacesuit," ed. Nikolay Moiseev, Nicolas Pillet, and Alain Chabot, Russian Space Web, last modified November 19, 2017, http://www.russianspaceweb.com/orlan_mks.html.

7. Zak, "Orlan MKS Spacesuit."

8. Cristoforetti, *Diary of an Apprentice Astronaut*, 115.

9. Cristoforetti, *Diary of an Apprentice Astronaut*, 115.

10. Cristoforetti, *Diary of an Apprentice Astronaut*, 114.

11. Lou Chen, "Taikonaut Zhai's Small Step Historical Leap for China," China View News, September 27, 2008, https://web.archive.org/web/20081001020959/http://news.xinhuanet.com/english/2008-09/27/content_10122420.htm.

12. Dave Mosher and Jenny Chang, "Here's Every Key Spacesuit NASA Astronauts Have Worn since the 1960s — and New Models That May Soon Arrive," Business Insider (Business Insider, March 26, 2019), https://www.businessinsider.com/spacesuit-design-history-timeline-changes-nasa-2018-3.

13. Hunter Hollins, "Forgotten Hardware: How to Urinate in a Spacesuit," *The American Physiological Society* 37, no. 2 (June 1, 2013): pp. 123-128, https://doi.org/https://journals.physiology.org/doi/full/10.1152/advan.00175.2012

14. Jon M. Chang, "The History of Urinating in Space," ABC News (ABC News Network, July 11, 2013), https://abcnews.go.com/Technology/history-urinating-space/story?id=19641585.

15. "Mercury Suit Gordon Cooper," December 14, 1962, photograph, NASA, http://www.hq.nasa.gov/office/pao/History/alsj/mercgem/mg-KSC-63PC-2.jpg.

16. "Buzz Aldrin on the Moon," July 20, 1969, photograph, NASA, https://flic.kr/p/8PU1qd.

17. NASA Content Administrator, "Facts About Spacesuits and Spacewalking," NASA (NASA, last modified July 5, 2018), https://www.nasa.gov/audience/foreducators/spacesuits/facts/index.html.

18. Terry Virts, *How to Astronaut: An Insider's Guide to Leaving Planet Earth* (New York, Workman Publishing, 2020), 61.

19. "ACES STS-130," January 21, 2010, photograph, NASA, http://mediaarchive.ksc.nasa.gov/detail.cfm?mediaid=45184.

20. Jason Daley, "Astronauts Test Out Their Sleek New SpaceX Flight Suits," Smithsonian.com (Smithsonian Institution, August 12, 2019), https://www.smithsonianmag.com/smart-news/astronauts-test-out-their-new-flight-suits-180972882/.

21. "SpaceX Spacesuit," August 22, 2017, photograph, NASA, https://images.nasa.gov/details-KSC-20180102-PH_SPX01_0010.

22. "Nasa SpaceX Launch: Evolution of the Spacesuit," BBC News (BBC, May 28, 2020), https://www.bbc.com/news/science-environment-52787365.

23. Holly Secon, "Elon Musk Said He Spent 3 to 4 Years Working on SpaceX's New Spacesuits and Hopes the Design Gets Kids 'Fired up' about Astronauts," Business Insider, May 28, 2020, https://www.businessinsider.com/elon-musk-design-spacex-spacesuits-worn-nasa-astronauts-2020-5.

24. Secon, "SpaceX's New Spacesuits."

25. "The Extravehicular Mobility Unit (EMU)," April, 2020, photograph, NASA, https://www.nasa.gov/image-feature/the-extravehicular-mobility-unit-emu.

26. David P. Cadogan, "The Past and Future Space Suit," American Scientist, March 27, 2019, https://www.americanscientist.org/article/the-past-and-future-space-suit.

27. Virts, How to Astronaut, 202.

28. Virts, How to Astronaut, 202.

29. Cristoforetti, Diary of an Apprentice Astronaut, 89.

30. Sara Aftab, "Ever Wondered How Hard Does An Astronaut Have To Bang To Break Glass Of His Helmet? Let Us Find Out," Wonderful Engineering, January 1, 2020, https://wonderfulengineering.com/strength-astronaut-helmet-glass/.

31. Chris Hadfield, "Spacewalking: Spacesuits," MasterClass.com (MasterClass), accessed May 28, 2021, https://www.masterclass.com/classes/chris-hadfield-teaches-space-exploration/chapters/spacewalking-spacesuits.

32. Cristoforetti, Diary of an Apprentice Astronaut, 139.

33. "Robert Frost's Answer to How Do Astronaut Space Helmets Work? How Is It That They Don't Steam up in Space? - Quora," Quora.com, accessed May 28, 2021, https://qr.ae/pGK0ag.

34. Scott Kelly, Endurance: A Year in Space, A Lifetime of Discovery (New York: Alfred A. Knopf, 2017), 280.

35. Administrator, "Facts About Spacesuits."

36. Kelly, Endurance, 273.

37. "My wrist mirror reflects my visor, which reflects the Earth," July 9, 2013, photograph, ESA/NASA, https://www.esa.int/ESA_Multimedia/Images/2013/07/My_wrist_mirror_refects_my_visor_which_reflects_the_Earth.

38. Cristoforetti, Diary of an Apprentice Astronaut, 146.

39. Tim Peake, Ask an Astronaut: My Guide to Life in Space (Little Brown and Company, 2017), 140.

40. "Astronaut Mark Lee floats free of tether during EVA," September 16, 1994, photograph, NASA, https://images.nasa.gov/details-STS064-45-014.

41. "Simplified Aid for EVA Rescue," May 29, 2014, photograph, NASA, https://www.nasa.gov/audience/foreducators/spacesuits/home/clickable_suit_nf.html.

42. Peake, Ask an Astronaut. 75-76.

43. "Orion Crew Survival System," NASA, October 15, 2019, photograph, https://images.nasa.gov/details-NHQ201910150020.

44. Gary Jordan and Chris Hansen, "Houston, We Have a Podcast, Ep 120: Artemis Spacesuits," ed. Norah Moran, NASA (NASA, April 15, 2021), https://www.nasa.gov/johnson/HWHAP/artemis-spacesuits.

45. "Artemis Generation Spacesuit Event," NASA, October 15, 2019, photograph, https://images.nasa.gov/details-NHQ201910150006.

46. Jordan and Hansen, "Artemis Spacesuits."

47. Jordan and Hansen, "Artemis Spacesuits."

48. Neel V. Patel, "Current Spacesuits Won't Cut It on the Moon. So NASA Made New Ones.," MIT Technology Review, December 29, 2020, https://www.technologyreview. com/2020/12/29/1015573/future-spacesuits-moon-mars-nasa-xemu/.

49. Brian Dunbar, "A Next Generation Spacesuit for the Artemis Generation of Astronauts," ed. Erin Mahoney, NASA (NASA, April 3, 2020), https://www.nasa.gov/feature/a-next-generation-spacesuit-for-the-artemis-generation-of-astronauts.

50. Dunbar, "Next Generation Spacesuit."

51. "A 21st Century Spacesuit," Boeing, accessed May 28, 2021, https://www.boeing.com/ space/starliner/#/spacesuit.

52. "Virgin Galactic Partners with Under Armour to Unveil the World's First Exclusive Spacewear System for Private Astronauts," Virgin Galactic, October 16, 2019, https://www. virgingalactic.com/articles/virgin-galactic-partners-with-under-armour-to-unveil-the-worlds-first-exclusive-spacewear-system-for-private-astronauts/.

SPACE STATIONS

Space stations are how humans are able to stay in space for extended periods of time. They allows us to study the effects of long-term space travel on the human body, as well as other scientific experiments that can only be done in that type of environment. Space stations have been used for both scientific and military purposes. Space stations have existed in space since 1971, and plans for additional space stations are in the works.

Retired Space Stations

THE SOVIET UNION'S SALYUT AND ALMAZ (1971-1977)

Salyut 1 was the world's first crewed space station. It was launched by the Soviet Union in 1971. Salyut means "salute" or "fireworks" in Russian. The Soviet Union had two different types of Salyut space stations, the civilian Soyuz space station and the ultra-secret military Almaz station. Almaz means "diamond" in Russian.

The Almaz program launched three space stations under the name of Salyut—Salyut 2, 3, and 5. The Salyut civilian program successfully launched Salyut 1, 4, 6, and 7.

Two more stations were launched, but were never given the Salyut name. Instead, they were known as the "Mir Core Module" and the "Zvezda Service Module." The Mir Core Module eventually became part of the modular Mir space station and the Zvezda Service Module became one of the first modules of the International Space Station.

Salyut 3 and Salyut 6 both had showers, but both showers proved frustrating to use and were abandoned. They were first turned into steam rooms, but eventually the plumbing was removed and the space was repurposed.[1]

SPACE STATION MIR (1986-2001)

In Russian, the word Mir has two meanings, "the world" and "peace." It was the first modular space station and was assembled in space.

View of the Russian Mir Space Station photographed by a crewmember of the fifth Shuttle/Mir docking mission, STS-81. Photo courtesy of NASA.[2]

Much of what was learned from Mir was applied to building the International Space Station.

During the 15-year life of Mir, it orbited the Earth 86,331 times, was visited by 104 people from 12 different nations and was occupied for 12.5 years. A total of 31 Soyuz spacecrafts and 11 space shuttle missions flew to Mir during its lifetime.

Mir had two toilets and a shower onboard. The special microgravity shower took a very long time to set up, use and then stow away. It was eventually turned into a steam room and finally removed completely so the space could be used for something else.

The Mir space station came to an end when it was deorbited in a controlled descent. What didn't burn up in the atmosphere during re-entry landed in the South Pacific Ocean.

AMERICA'S SKYLAB (1973-1979)

America's first space station was the Skylab, which housed three separate crews: Skylab 2, 3 and 4. Skylab could accommodate a crew of three and was built with several lessons learned from the Apollo program. Previous U.S. spacecraft hadn't been constructed for comfort over long periods of time. But Skylab was meant to be occupied for months at a time. Each crew member had a private sleeping area about the size of a small walk-in closet that included a sleeping bag, privacy curtain and locker. The food on Skylab was a huge improvement over previous space food. Exercise equipment and a place to eat were also part of Skylab.

Skylab was a research laboratory, and three crews combined to conduct 270 experiments. One experiment was studying the crew themselves! The crew lived onboard Skylab for 28, 56 and 85 days, respectively. One of the biggest things scientists learned was how the astronauts' bodies and minds fared during long-duration spaceflights.[3]

The final Skylab crew left in February 1974. Skylab remained empty until it lost altitude over time and re-entered Earth's atmosphere on July 11, 1979. While most of it disintegrated upon re-entry, debris that didn't burn up was scattered across the Indian Ocean and Western Australia.

TAKING SHOWERS IN SPACE

Like the Soviet space stations, Salyut 3 and 6, Skylab had a zero-gravity shower onboard. It had foot restraints on what could be considered the floor of the shower and a cylinder-shaped curtain that could be extended from floor to ceiling. A vacuum system was used to suck away the water. It took 2.5 hours to complete a shower on Skylab. This included the set-up, the shower itself and then the clean-up. In addition to the shower, Skylab had 420 towels onboard that had color-coded stitching for each crew member.[4]

CHINA'S TIANGONG-1 AND TIANGONG-2 (2011-2019)

Tiangong means "heaven" or "celestial palace" in Chinese. Tiangong-1 was China's first space station, which launched in September 2011 and orbited Earth until April 2018.[5] Tiangong-2 launched in 2016 and re-entered Earth's atmosphere as planned in 2019.[6] Both of these short-lived space stations were successful tests. They were meant to prepare for a larger and longer-lived space station called the Tiangong space station, which was launched April 29, 2021 and is currently being assembled as of June 2021.

International Space Station in 2020. Photo by NASA.[7]

INTERNATIONAL SPACE STATION

The International Space Station, or ISS for short, is the most expensive object ever created! The ISS has cost a total of $150 billion and counting. It costs NASA about $4 billion a year to operate.[8] It's also the only object that is made up of components that were created by different countries and assembled in space.[9]

The ISS got its start back in 1984 when US president Ronald Reagan announced that NASA was designing a space station called Freedom. The goal was to put it into orbit within 10 years. Freedom never got off the ground, but in 1993—nine years after Reagan's announcement—President Clinton announced that Freedom would merge with Mir-2, a space station that was first being planned by the Soviet Union, but now was under Russia's control. Soon after, three other space agencies got involved: CSA (Canada), JAXA (Japan), and ESA (22 European member states).

The first two modules were joined together in December of 1998, when the Unity Node 1 module was joined to the Russian FGB, or Zarya, module. Almost two years later, on November 2, 2000, the first crew moved into the space station.[10]

Since then, over 240 astronauts, cosmonauts and space tourists from 19 different nations have visited the ISS—some more than once! The International Space Station is in excellent shape, with a planned lifespan well beyond 2030.[11] Currently the plan is to discontinue funding in a few years and to do a controlled de-orbit, like space stations in the past, possibly in 2030.[12]

Watch a live video stream and see what the crew onboard the ISS see as they orbit the earth: https://www.asc-csa.gc.ca/eng/iss/watch-live.asp

  DID YOU KNOW?

20 YEARS WITHOUT THE ENTIRE HUMAN POPULATION ON EARTH

Since November, 2, 2000, astronauts have lived continuously onboard the International Space Station. That means the human race hasn't had all of its people on the planet at one time since that date!

Artist rendering of China's Tiangong space station with Tianhe core module in the middle, Tianzhou-2 cargo spacecraft on the left, and Tianzhou-3 cargo spacecraft on the right and the Shenzhou-13 crewed spacecraft at nadir. Image rendering by Shujianyang, CC BY-SA 4.0, via Wikimedia Commons.

CHINA'S TIANGONG SPACE STATION

China's third space station, officially known as the Tiangong space station, is expected to be three modules, making it about the size of Mir and about one-fifth of the size of the ISS. China launched the core module called Tianhe, which means "harmony of the heavens" on April 29, 2021. This core module is the main living space and life support for the future crews who will live onboard.[13]

Future Space Stations

LUNAR GATEWAY

NASA, ESA, CSA and JAXA have all agreed to contribute to the planned Lunar Gateway mini space station that will orbit the Moon. Its purpose is to serve as a staging point for lunar exploration. It will make possible multiple longer-duration trips to the Moon's surface. The Lunar Gateway will have a habitation module, communication hub, science lab and a place to park reusable lunar landers.[14] The current plan is to launch the first two Gateway modules in 2024.

LUNAR ORBITAL STATION

Russia has its own plans to put a space station in the Moon's orbit. This is called the Lunar Orbital Station (LOS). Russia's plans for the Moon include an orbital station with a detachable lunar lander and a base on the lunar surface.[15]

ESA ASTRONAUTS LEARNING MANDARIN

The European Space Agency partners with both Russia and the US when it comes to space travel. They're also partnering with China, and have sent a few of their astronauts to train with China's taikonauts. Those astronauts are learning Mandarin in preparation for trips to the future Chinese space station, Tiangong, in the coming years.[16]

NOTES

1. David M. Harland, *The Story of Space Station Mir* (New York, NY: Springer New York, 2005), 134.

2. "Russian Space Station Mir," NASA, January 1, 1997, photograph, https://images.nasa.gov/details-9702655.

3. Elizabeth Howell, "Skylab: First U.S. Space Station," Space.com, July 11, 2018, https://www.space.com/19607-skylab.html.

4. Leland F. Belew, "Ch. 5 The First Manned Period," in *Skylab, Our First Space Station* (Washington, D.C: Scientific and Technical Information Office, National Aeronautics and Space Administration, 1977), https://history.nasa.gov/SP-400/ch5.htm.

5. Lily Kuo, "Tiangong-1 Crash: Chinese Space Station Comes down in Pacific Ocean," The Guardian (Guardian News and Media, April 2, 2018), https://www.theguardian.com/world/2018/apr/02/tiangong-1-crash-china-space-station.

6. Andrew Jones, "China Set to Carry out Controlled Deorbiting of Tiangong-2 Space Lab," SpaceNews, July 12, 2019, https://spacenews.com/china-set-to-carry-out-controlled-deorbiting-of-tiangong-2-space-lab/.

7. "International Space Station," NASA, November 2020, photograph, https://www.nasa.gov/sites/default/files/s132e012209_sm.jpg.

8. Michael Sheetz, "NASA wants companies to develop and build new space stations, with p to $400 million up for grabs," CNBC.com, March 27, 2021, https://www.cnbc.com/2021/03/27/nasa-commercial-leo-destinations-project-for-private-space-stations.html.

9. Scott Kelly, *Endurance: A Year in Space, A Lifetime of Discovery* (New York: Alfred A. Knopf, 2017), 69.

10. "Robert Frost's Answer to How Long Has the International Space Station Been in Orbit? – Quora," Quora, accessed May 30, 2021, https://qr.ae/pG8ns2.

11. Christian Davenport, "The International Space Station Can't Stay up There Forever. Will Privately Run, Commercial Replacements Be Ready in Time?," The Washington Post (WP Company, December 23, 2020), https://www.washingtonpost.com/technology/2020/12/23/space-station-replace-biden/.

12. Bill Nelson (@SenBillNelson), "The Senate Just Passed My Bill to Help Commercial Space Companies Launch More than One Rocket a Day from Florida! This Is an Exciting Bill That Will Help Create Jobs and Keep Rockets Roaring from the Cape. It Also Extends the International Space Station to 2030!," Twitter (Twitter, December 20, 2018), https://twitter.com/SenBillNelson/status/1075840067569139712.

13. "China Launches First Tiangong Space Station Module: DW: 29.04.2021," DW.COM, April 29, 2021, https://www.dw.com/en/china-launches-first-tiangong-space-station-module/a-57369206.

14. Brian Dunbar, "Competition Seeks Concepts for Gateway, Human Exploration," ed. Shanessa Jackson, NASA (NASA, last modified September 11, 2018), https://www.nasa.gov/feature/competition-seeks-university-concepts-for-gateway-and-deep-space-exploration-capabilities.

15. Anatoly Zak, "Lunar Orbital Station, LOS," RussianSpaceWeb.com, last modified January 22, 2020, http://www.russianspaceweb.com/los.html.

16. Richard Hollingham, "Why Europe's Astronauts Are Learning Chinese," BBC Future (BBC, June 27, 2018), https://www.bbc.com/future/article/20180626-why-europes-astronauts-are-learning-chinese.

THE INTERNATIONAL SPACE STATION

The International Space Station, or ISS for short, is the biggest man-made structure in space, the most expensive single object ever constructed and a remarkable achievement of technology and international cooperation.[1]

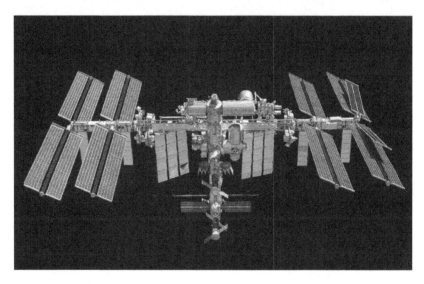

International Space Station as seen from the SpaceX Crew Dragon Endeavour during a fly around on November 8, 2021. Photo by NASA.[2]

How It Started

THE BEGINNING

In 1984, US president Ronald Reagan, announced during his State of the Union address that NASA was designing a space station called Freedom, to be put into space within ten years. After nine years of resistance from Congress and several budget cuts, Freedom hadn't made much progress. In 1993, President Bill Clinton announced that the station would be merged with the Mir-2, the Russian Federal Space Agency's proposed space station. Other space agencies representing Europe, Japan and Canada partnered with Russia and the US to come together as fifteen countries and five space agencies to create what we now know as the International Space Station.[3]

THE MISSION OF THE INTERNATIONAL SPACE STATION
1. To build international and commercial human exploration partnerships
2. Enable long-duration human spaceflight beyond low-Earth orbit
3. Return benefits to humanity through basic and applied research
4. Facilitate the development of a commercial market in low-Earth orbit

MULTI-NATIONAL COLLABORATIVE PROJECT
The International Space Station is the only object with components that were manufactured by different countries and assembled in space.[4] Fifteen countries cooperate on a daily basis to operate the International Space Station.

THE FIVE SPACE AGENCIES & FIFTEEN COUNTRIES
The five space agencies that partner together and represent fifteen countries in total are:
- Russia's Roscosmos
- USA's NASA
- Canada's CSA
- Japan's JAXA
- Europe's ESA, representing these 11 member states:
  Belgium
  Denmark
  France
  Germany
  Italy

The Netherlands
Norway
Spain
Sweden
Switzerland
United Kingdom[5]

Basic Facts & Figures

HOW MANY FLIGHTS DID IT TAKE TO BUILD?

It took more than 100 launches to get the space station components into orbit and more than 100 spacewalks to assemble them. The first people to stay on the ISS for a long-duration mission arrived on November 2, 2000.

HIGH IN THE SKY

The ISS is roughly 260 miles (418 km) above the Earth's surface. This works out to be just a little bit farther than the distance between Washington, DC and New York City, or the width of the state of California.

SPEED RACER

The ISS travels at a speed of 5 miles per second (8 km per second), or roughly 17,500 mph (28,100 kph) while in orbit.[6]

SUNRISES & SUNSETS

In a single 24-hour-long day, the space station makes about 16 orbits of Earth and travels through 16 sunrises and sunsets. If you want to get super technical, it circles the Earth roughly every 93 minutes, which means it completes 15.5 orbits in one day.

PRESSURIZED MODULE LENGTH

The modules where the crew can live is 167 feet (50.9 meters) long. This is the same length as six London buses lined up end to end, or about half as tall as the Statue of Liberty.[7]

SOLAR ARRAY LENGTH

The ISS has eight pairs of solar arrays and each one is 240 feet (73 meters) long. This is about as tall as a giant sequoia tree or the length of the world's largest passenger airplane, the Airbus 380. These eight solar arrays can generate 84 to 120 kilowatts of power during orbital daytime.[8] For comparison, a microwave uses around 1.2 kilowatts and an electric tea kettle needs 1.8 kilowatts of power.[9]

HOW LONG IS IT?

The ISS's central truss is 357.5 feet (108.8 meters) long. This is 1 yard shorter than the length of an American football field, when including the endzones.

HOW MUCH DOES IT WEIGH?

This is kind of a trick question, since it's currently weightless! But the total mass of the space station is 925,335 lbs (419,725 kg). This is about six times as heavy as a space shuttle or four times as heavy as a blue whale, which is the largest mammal on Earth.[10]

CAN BE SEEN FROM EARTH WITHOUT A TELESCOPE

The massive solar panels on the station make it easy to see the space station fly by at dusk or dawn when the sun reflects off of the panels. It's the largest human-made object in space and can be seen by the naked eye from most places on Earth. Its orbital path takes it over 90% of the Earth's population, so chances are you can see it where you live. NASA has a site specifically for spotting the space station at: http://spotthestation.nasa.gov

NO FLASHING STROBE LIGHTS

One way to tell if you're looking at the space station or an airplane is to check to see if it's blinking. The International Space Station does not blink.[11]

SEEING IT WITH A TELESCOPE

Depending on the level of magnification of your telescope, you may be able to see more than a fast-moving light across the sky. If you want to see photographs of the space station taken from a telescope from Earth, check out Thierry Legault's website: http://www.astrophoto. fr/

Legault is an engineer who lives in the suburbs of Paris. He has some impressive photos taken from his telescope of the space shuttle, the space station and even an astronaut working on the space station!

MILLIONS OF LINES OF COMPUTER CODE

No one flies the ISS. It's flown and run by computer software. In just the US segment of the ISS, there are more than 1.5 million lines of flight software code that run on 44 computers. On the ground, there's more than 3 million lines of code that support the flight software code. If human intervention was needed, it would be done by laptop computers on the station or on the ground.[12]

HOW THE ISS STAYS IN ORBIT

While the ISS does have its own thrusters and fuel, they are very rarely used. Normally, the station uses the orbital maneuvering thrusters of other spacecraft that are docked to it, like the Progress cargo ships.[13] Mission control calculates how long a ship should fire its engine and sends the command that boosts the ISS back into the proper orbit, or maneuvers it out of the way of space debris that might be heading in its direction.

NOT YOUR NORMAL LIVING QUARTERS

The space station is the largest space station ever built and is larger than your average six-bedroom house. It currently has six sleeping quarters, two bathrooms, and a gym with a treadmill, stationary bike, special weightless weightlifting machine and a great view! The ISS also has toilets that can recycle urine into pure, filtered water.

While there is a makeshift table in the module that astronauts use as their dining room, there are no seats. Microgravity makes sitting difficult!

PANORAMIC VIEWS & BULLET-PROOF WINDOWS

One of the most popular features of the ISS is its 360° bay window, courtesy of the European Space Agency. Astronauts normally refer to it as the cupola, which means "dome." The cupola's seven glass windows are made of four separate layers. Each layer is made from bulletproof material to protect astronauts from the occasional micrometeoroid that passes by. Because of its shape, its multiple windows and how they're configured, the cupola has been compared to the Millennium Falcon's cockpit window in *Star Wars*.[14]

View of the Cupola from outside. Astronaut Kayla Barron smiles from inside the ISS's "window to the world."[15] Photo courtesy of NASA.

View of the Earth from within the Cupola. Photo taken by Astronaut Scott Kelly. Photo courtesy of NASA.[16]

THE SOUNDS OF THE ISS

Noisy machinery recycles CO_2, urine and sweat. And astronauts can hear fellow crew members exercising. But there are other noises unique to the ISS.

It's common to hear the space station creaking and snapping as its metal expands or contracts going into and out of sunlight. The space station orbits the Earth 217 to 248 miles (350 to 400 km) above Earth. When it's in the Earth's shadow, the ISS can reach temperatures of -184°F (-120°C). In the sun, the temperature rises to 302°F (150°C).

Micrometeorites and tiny bits of space debris do hit the station from time to time, and the crews can hear the pings as they hit.[17]

OUTSIDE THE SPACE STATION

Over 20 different research experiments can be performed outside the space station at the same time. There has been earth-sensing equipment, particle physics experiments like the Alpha Magnetic Spectrometer-02—which looks for evidence of dark matter in the universe—and more.[18]

LOTS OF PARKING SPOTS

The ISS can connect with up to eight spacecrafts at the same time.

VARIABLE COMMUTE

The time it takes for a spacecraft to get from Earth to the ISS varies. A spacecraft can arrive as quickly as around three hours. And the space shuttle typically docked with the ISS within 24 hours. But sometimes it takes longer because of orbital mechanics, and the difficulty in catching up with a space station that is traveling at 17,500 mph (28,000 kph) at an average orbit altitude of 250 miles (400 km). On occasion, it takes up to three days to get to the space station,[19] which can make for a long commute in cramped conditions.

The fastest rendezvous to date was on October 14, 2020, by the crew of Soyuz MS-17. They did it in three hours—or two orbits—which is about half the time it normally takes.[20]

HOW MANY PASSENGERS?

As of April 2021, there have been over 243 people from 19 different countries since it was first inhabited starting on November 2, 2000. Many have visited more than once.[21]

Six people have visited the station four separate times: Gennady Padalka and Oleg Kononenko from Russia and NASA astronauts Jeffrey N. Williams, Frederick W. Sturckow, Richard A. Mastracchio and Mark Kelly.

Only two men have been to the ISS five times: Yuri Malenchenko and Fyodor Yurchikhin from Russia.[22]

MOST TIME ON THE ISS

Astronaut Peggy Whitson holds the female record for spending the most time onboard the International Space Station with a total of 665 days, 22 hours and 22 minutes over the course of five expeditions.[23] Cosmonaut Gennady Padalka holds the overall record for spending the most time on the ISS, with a total of 679 days, 18 hours and 58 minutes over seven expeditions.[24]

SPACEWALKS

Since 1998, there have been more than 227 spacewalks to assemble and maintain the ISS. Of those, 173 were done in American EVA spacesuits and 54 of them were done in Russian Orlan spacesuits.[25]

Parts & Pieces

GIANT EMPTY SODA CANS

The ISS is a modular space station, which means it's made up of different sections called modules. This means modules can be added or removed.

From the outside, the ISS looks like giant, empty soda cans attached end-to-end. Along the longer part, there are five modules: three American and two Russian modules. There are several offshoot modules from Europe, Japan, Russia and the U.S. that are connected to the left and right (or port and starboard) sides. The two Russian offshoot modules are connected up (zenith) and down (nadir).[26]

BUILT IN SPACE

The space station was built in space using robotic arms and lots of spacewalks. It was never built out completely on Earth. Some pieces were added on later and had to fit. The ISS itself is a massive global technological achievement.

THE TWO SEGMENTS OF THE ISS

The station is divided into two segments: the Russian Orbital Segment run by Russia and the United States Orbital segment that is run by the United States and several other countries.

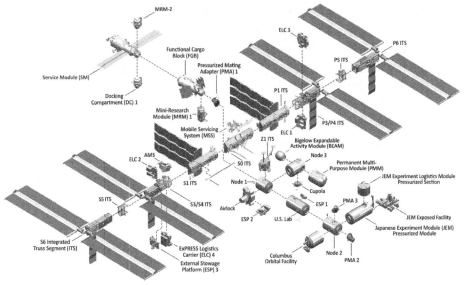

Exploded view to show the parts of the International Space Station. Image courtesy of NASA.[27]

DIFFERENT ELECTRICS & FIRE EXTINGUISHERS

The Russian segment uses low-voltage electrical systems and foam fire extinguishers. The rest of the ISS has 120V systems and carbon dioxide extinguishers are preferred there.[28]

UNLIKELY FIRES

Nearly everything aboard the ISS is made of non-flammable material or kept in fireproof bags. But the crews are trained and prepared for emergencies—even unlikely fires.[29]

FUNCTIONAL CARGO BLOCK "ZARYA"

This was the first module of the ISS. It was named Zarya, which means "dawn" or "sunrise" in Russian to represent the dawn of a new era of international cooperation in space. This module is also known as the Functional Cargo Block (FCB). It was originally used to provide power, storage, and propulsion in the early years, but now it's mainly used for storage.

THE SERVICE MODULE – ZVEZDA

Zvezda in Russian means "star." This was the first multipurpose research laboratory on the ISS. Zvezda is where the two crew quarters are for the cosmonauts in the Russian segment. This is the module where the ISS crews will gather in case of emergencies. It has a treadmill, exercise bike, toilet, a kitchen with a refrigerator, a freezer and a table. It has 14 windows, with a window in each of the two crew quarters.

NODE 1 – UNITY

The is the module that connects the US and Russian segments of the station. The crew uses this module mainly for the kitchen and living room. This was the first ISS module built by the US.

NODE 2 – HARMONY

Node 2 connects the U.S., Europe and Japan laboratory module. Four of the six telephone booth-sized crew quarters are located here. The U.S. astronaut's crew quarters are in Node 2 and the Russians have the other two crew quarters in the Russian segment.

NODE 3 – TRANQUILITY

The noisiest area of the ISS is in Node 3, due to the life support equipment it houses. These systems remove carbon dioxide, recycle urine and sweat and produce oxygen through water electrolysis. This is also where the toilet, other exercise equipment and the cupola are. The name Tranquility is in honor of the first lunar landing of Apollo 11 on the Sea of Tranquility.

U.S. LAB – DESTINY

Destiny is NASA's permanent orbital research station, and the first one they've had since the Skylab space station. Destiny has a 20-inch (50.8-cm) telescope-quality glass window that's used for Earth science observations. There are 24 payload racks inside of Destiny, with six on each side of the module. The Destiny module made an appearance in the 2013 movie *Gravity*.

ESA LAB – COLUMBUS

This lab is attached to Node 2 and is Europe's largest contribution to the International Space Station. The lab is able to conduct experiments inside the module, but also on the outside in the vacuum of space. Columbus has 10 science racks—also called payload racks—inside and four payload platforms that can be attached outside. Each rack is the size of a telephone booth. Activities are controlled by the Columbus Control Center near Munich, Germany.[30]

JAPAN LAB – KIB

This is the Japanese Experiment Module, or JEM, but it has been nicknamed Kibō, pronounced key-bow, which means "hope" in Japanese. This is the largest single ISS module. It's attached to Node 2. Kibō is where many of the onboard press conferences take place.

Kibō has 23 payload racks, 10 for science experiments and 13 for storage and Kibō systems. There are 12 payload platforms that fully expose experiments to the vacuum of space.[31]

MINI-RESEARCH MODULE 1

The Rassvet, or MRM1, is mainly used for cargo storage. The name Rassvet means "first light" in Russian. It's also a docking port for the Soyuz or Progress spacecrafts.

View of the Earth as seen from inside the Cupola. Photo by Karen Nyberg courtesy of NASA.

CUPOLA – THE BAY WINDOW ON THE WORLD

Cupola means "dome" in Italian, which is an appropriate description of the dome-shaped module! It's the "Bay window on the world" that offers panoramic views of the Earth with its seven bullet-proof windows. The ISS Observation Deck is attached to the Earth-facing port of the Tranquility module and has been compared to the Millennium Falcon cockpit windows, of Star Wars fame. The windows have shutters to protect them from contamination, space debris and micrometeorites.

The seven-windowed observation deck is also the ISS robotic control station that controls the Canadarm2. This is where astronauts can see and maneuver the robotic arm to grab and release cargo ships and assist spacewalking astronauts.[32]

LEONARDO

Its full name is the Leonardo Permanent Multipurpose Module, or PMM for short. It's mainly used as a closet for storage and is the personal hygiene area for the astronauts on the US side of the ISS.

BEAM

The BEAM, or Bigelow Expandable Activity Module, is an expandable and inflatable space station module that is used as a temporary module. It's lightweight and requires minimal room on a rocket. It was added to the ISS to test if it might be something that could be taken in future deep space travel. The BEAM has been described as a large closet with padded white walls with equipment and sensors. The shell is made of a flexible Kevlar-like material and is designed to protect it from debris and micrometeoroid impact and radiation.[33]

AIRLOCKS

The station has four airlocks where equipment and crew members can move between the station and open space. One airlock is just for equipment. Two airlocks—Poisk (Explore) and Pirs (Pier)—are for EVAs in Russian Orlan spacesuits and one airlock is for EVAs in American EMU spacesuits.[34] The Quest Airlock can support both U.S. and Russian spacesuits.[35] The Russian airlocks are docking ports for the Russian segment of the ISS.

CANADARM2 ROBOTIC ARM

Canadarm2 is a robotic arm that is 56 feet (17 meters) long. It was used to assemble the ISS, module by module entirely in space. It's about the size of a large redwood tree. It is used to move supplies, equipment and even astronauts. It's also used to grab free-flying cargo spacecraft and attach them to the ISS.

DEXTRE ROBOTIC ARM

Dextre has two arms and a robotic torso with lights. It houses video equipment and power tools. Because this robot can perform tasks that require fine and precise control, it can do a lot of the work that astronauts would do on spacewalks. Dextre can be operated by both astronauts from the station and people on Earth.

MOBILE BASE SYSTEM

The MBS is a moveable base on rails that runs the length of the station's main truss. It is used as a base for the Canadarm2 and Dextre and can be moved along the outside of the station, making it possible to reach all parts of the US segment.

JAPAN'S ROBOTIC ARM

Japan has their own robotic arm that is permanently attached at one end to the Kibō module. It is used to service the exposed experiments or support maintenance tasks on the Kibō lab.[36]

FUTURE COMPONENTS

Several components and modules are planned to launch in the next few years.

EUROPE'S ROBOTIC ARM

In July 2021, Europe launched a robotic arm to the ISS. It's the only robotic arm that can attach to and work with the Russina segment. And Russia is planning to launch their Multipurpose Laboratory Module (MLM) and a ball-shaped module called Prichal, or Uzlovoy Module. This will give the Russian segment additional docking ports. Russia also has two science power modules they plan to launch after 2024.

AXIOM SEGMENT

Axiom Space is building a commercial habitation module for the ISS that it plans to launch in 2024. It will connect to the Harmony node and provide crew habitat, a research and manufacturing facility and a large-windowed Earth observatory. NASA only contracted with Axiom to build one module. But Axiom has plans to build an entire commercial segment with five modules that will allow for larger crews and private spaceflights.[37]

TRUSS – THE BACKBONE OF THE STATION

The aluminum and stainless-steel Truss, or Integrated Truss Structure (ITS), is made of 10 separate segments that, combined, measure 365 feet (108.5 meters) long. The eight solar arrays and radiators are connected to the Truss. The center truss, also called S0 truss, is attached to the top of the Destiny module. It sends power from the solar arrays to the modules and conducts heat away from the modules.

POWERED BY THE SUN

The space station has eight massive solar arrays that have the ability to twist and spin so they can follow the sun. These solar arrays are out away from the living quarters and out of the way of the docking areas so they won't be damaged when space ships dock and undock.

HEATING

The space station has large radiators that act much like radiators found in older homes. They collect heated liquid from around the station's living quarters and pump the liquid into the radiators, which radiate the heat out into space. To pump the heat away from the sun, the radiators are able to turn away from the heat of the sun.

ORIENTATION

The ISS is oriented so that the long flat part is parallel to the horizon. This is the most stable and energy-efficient position. It's also best suited for communication with ground control as it orbits around Earth. The solar panels can then move to follow the sun independently from the station's motion.

SIZE MATTERS

The US Modules were carried up by the space shuttle, so the size of those modules was determined by the size of the shuttle's cargo bay.

The Russian modules were built in Moscow and then transported by train to Baikonur, Kazakhstan, where they were launched on top of rockets. The size of the Russian modules was determined based on the height and width of the railway overpasses from Moscow to Baikonur. The module length was based on whether it would be able to ride on a railcar that could make it around the railway's corners.[38]

Life Support Systems Onboard the ISS

Astronauts and cosmonauts live aboard the ISS by using both supplies brought up from Earth—including oxygen, water, and food—and onboard systems that can regenerate oxygen and water. As humans begin to further explore space, the need to be more self-sufficient and rely less on Earth resupply trips will become critical.

OXYGEN

The space station has machines onboard that are able to take CO_2 from the air, separate the oxygen from the carbon and recycle the oxygen back into the space station, making it available to breathe.

Oxygen is brought to the space station in multiple ways. It can arrive as the air inside the cargo ships themselves. Sometimes the cargo ships are over-pressurized, which provides a little extra oxygen when depressurized. Other times, actual canisters of liquid oxygen are brought up as cargo.

WATER

Water is recycled onboard as much as possible. Humidity in the air is collected, and the gaseous water vapor is turned into liquid water. This water is purified before it can be drinkable.

Urine is mostly water, and engineers have figured out a way to separate out the water from the rest, purify it, and make it drinkable. Today, about 90% of the ISS's water is recycled—which is better than it's ever been. But in order for humans to make it to Mars, the goal is to recycle 100% of the water. Currently every cargo ship that visits the ISS carries air and water. But that won't be possible on Mars![39]

PURIFICATION SYSTEM

The ISS's purification system collects the water from the urine, the humidity and any waste water from experiments. It then spins the water to remove larger particles like sediment. Then it runs the water through complex filters and treats it chemically. Finally, the water is clean enough to drink and use to rehydrate food onboard.

SEVEN TONS OF SUPPLIES

Crews onboard the ISS need many things, including oxygen, food, clothes, water and experiments to work on while in space. It takes seven tons of supplies to support a crew of three onboard the ISS for six months in space. Supplies arrive in resupply cargo vehicles such as the Russian Progress cargo ships, the European Automated Transfer Vehicle, Japanese Kounotori cargo ship, Cygnus and SpaceX Cargo Dragon spacecrafts.[40]

NOTES

1. Scott Kelly, *Endurance: A Year in Space, A Lifetime of Discovery* (New York: Alfred A. Knopf, 2017), 23.

2. "The Station pictured from SpaceX Crew Dragon," NASA, November 8, 2021, photograph, https://www.nasa.gov/image-feature/the-station-pictured-from-the-spacex-crew-dragon-0.

3. Kelly, *Endurance*, 23.

4. Kelly, *Endurance*, 69.

5. Brian Dunbar, "International Cooperation," ed. Mark Garcia, NASA (NASA, October 15, 2020), https://www.nasa.gov/mission_pages/station/cooperation/index.html.

6. NASA, *Celebrating 20 Years of Human Presence on the ISS*, November 2020, Infographic, https://www.nasa.gov/sites/default/files/styles/full_width_feature/public/thumbnails/image/iss20_infographic_skye_full_20200702_0.jpg.

7. "The Measure of Things - 167 Feet," The Measure of Things, accessed May 30, 2021, https://www.themeasureofthings.com/results.php?comp=distance&unit=ft&amt=167&sort=pr&p=2.

8. Mark Garcia, "New Solar Arrays to Power NASA's International Space Station Research," NASA, last modified April 19, 2021, https://www.nasa.gov/feature/new-solar-arrays-to-power-nasa-s-international-space-station-research.

9. Brian Dunbar, "International Space Station Facts and Figures," ed. Mark Garcia, NASA (NASA, March 13, 2021), https://www.nasa.gov/feature/facts-and-figures.

10. "The Measure of Things - 925,335 Pounds," The Measure of Things, accessed May 30, 2021, https://www.themeasureofthings.com/results.php?amt=925335&comp=weight&unit=lbs&searchTerm=925%2C335%2Bpounds.

11. Tim Peake, *Ask an Astronaut: My Guide to Life in Space* (Little Brown and Company, 2017), 87.

12. Kelly, *Endurance*, 68.

13. "Andrew McGregor's Answer to Why Doesn't the Space Station Run out of Fuel to Make Its Course Corrections? Is Fresh Fuel Delivered on Visits to the ISS? – Quora," Quora, accessed May 30, 2021, https://qr.ae/pGN4Ag.

14. "First Photos: Space Station's Observation Deck Unveiled," National Geographic, February 18, 2010, https://www.nationalgeographic.com/science/article/100218-international-space-station-cupola-iss-obama-nasa-pictures.

15. "Astronaut Kayla Barron smiles while peering out from a cupola window," NASA, January 24, 2022, photograph, https://www.nasa.gov/image-feature/astronaut-kayla-barron-smiles-while-peering-out-from-a-cupola-window.

16. "Astronaut Scott Kelly in the Cupola," NASA, June 4, 2015, photograph, https://www.nasa.gov/image-feature/astronaut-scott-kelly-in-the-cupola.

17. "Frequently Asked Questions – Astronauts," CSA (Canadian Space Agency), accessed May 30, 2021, https://www.asc-csa.gc.ca/eng/astronauts/faq.asp.

18. "Alpha Magnetic Spectrometer – 02," Space Station Research Explorer on NASA.gov (NASA), accessed May 30, 2021, https://www.nasa.gov/mission_pages/station/research/experiments/explorer/Investigation.html#id=729.

19. *How Long Does It Take to Get to the ISS?*, YouTube (NASA, 2013), https://youtu.be/SeMvJoUm2Q.

20. Hanneke Weitering, "A Soyuz Capsule Just Made a Record-Breaking 3-Hour Flight to the International Space Station," Space.com, October 14, 2020, https://www.space.com/soyuz-makes-fastest-space-station-crew-flight-record.

21. Brian Dunbar, "Visitors to the Station by Country," ed. Mark Garcia, NASA (NASA, last modified April 27, 2021), https://www.nasa.gov/feature/visitors-to-the-station-by-country/.

22. Dunbar, "Visitors to the Station by Country."

23. "Astronaut Biography: Peggy Whitson," Space Facts, accessed May 30, 2021, http://www.spacefacts.de/bios/astronauts/english/whitson_peggy.htm.

24. "Cosmonaut Biography: Gennadi Padalka," Space Facts, accessed May 30, 2021, http://www.spacefacts.de/bios/cosmonauts/english/padalka_gennadi.htm.

25. NASA, "Celebrating 20 Years."

26. Kelly, *Endurance*, 71.

27. NASA, "ISS Configuration Exploded View," Illustration, accessed May 30, 2021, https://www.nasa.gov/sites/default/files/thumbnails/image/iss_config_exploded_view_page_0.jpg.

28. Samantha Cristoforetti, *Diary of an Apprentice Astronaut*, trans. Jill Foulston (Penguin, 2020), 153-154, Kindle.

29. Cristoforetti, *Diary of an Apprentice Astronaut*, 154.

30. "Columbus Laboratory," ESA (European Space Agency), accessed May 30, 2021, http://www.esa.int/Science_Exploration/Human_and_Robotic_Exploration/Columbus/Columbus_laboratory.

31. "About Kibo," JAXA (Japan Aerospace Exploration Agency, August 29, 2008), https://iss.jaxa.jp/en/kibo/about/kibo/jpm/.

32. National Geographic, "Space Station's Observation Deck Unveiled."

33. Brian Dunbar, "Background and Frequently Asked Questions about BEAM," ed. Erin Mahoney, NASA (NASA, August 6, 2017), https://www.nasa.gov/feature/beam-facts-figures-faqs.

34. Cristoforetti, *Diary of an Apprentice Astronaut*, 377.

35. "Reference Guide to the International Space Station," NASA, September 2015, https://www.nasa.gov/sites/default/files/atoms/files/np-2015-05-022-jsc-iss-guide-2015-update-111015-508c.pdf.

36. "Remote Manipulator System," JAXA, accessed May 30, 2021, https://web.archive.org/web/20080320035809/http://kibo.jaxa.jp/en/about/kibo/rms/.

37. Alan Boyle, "NASA Clears Axiom Space to Put Commercial Habitat on Space Station, with Boeing on the Team," GeekWire, January 27, 2020, https://www.geekwire.com/2020/nasa-clears-axiom-space-put-commercial-habitat-space-station-boeings-help/.

38. Chris Hadfield, "The ISS: Conception, Design, and Construction," MasterClass (MasterClass), accessed May 30, 2021, https://www.masterclass.com/classes/chris-hadfield-teaches-space-exploration/chapters/the-iss-conception-design-and-construction.

39. Chris Hadfield, "The ISS: Life Support Systems," MasterClass (MasterClass), accessed May 30, 2021, https://www.masterclass.com/classes/chris-hadfield-teaches-space-exploration/chapters/the-iss-life-support-systems.

40. Peake, *Ask an Astronaut*: 87.

LIFE ON THE ISS

MOVING THROUGH TIMEZONES

Do you ever wonder what time it is onboard the International Space Station (ISS) when it experiences 16 sunsets and sunrises every 24 hours? The clocks on the ISS are on GMT +0 (Greenwich Mean Time) or UTC+0 (Universal Time), which is the time at the Prime Meridian in Greenwich, London. Random fact, Iceland also happens to be on GMT+0 despite being far off in the Noth Atlantic. There is no daylight savings time on the space station or in Iceland. Japan and Russia don't observe daylight savings time, either, so that normally works out well for them.[1]

Since Mission Control centers in Houston, Texas; Huntsville, Alabama; and Munich, Germany do observe daylight savings time, the times for activities and experiments scheduled onboard the ISS can sometimes change.

The choice to use UTC time isn't because using a universal time reference for the International Space Station has a nice ring to it, or because of operational or technical considerations. It's all about the commute for the Mission Control team members in Moscow. It's important that the ISS astronauts' work day doesn't finish too late in Moscow time. If they end after 11 p.m., the Mission Control specialists won't be able to take the metro home because it closes!

Since people in Houston drive, there isn't the same reliance on the train, and starting a shift at one in the morning is a lot less logistically problematic. The Mission Control team members in Europe find themselves in the middle and many of them are on the same time zone as the space station. [2]

TEMPERATURES ONBOARD THE ISS

Inside the American segment, the temperatures can be between 64.5°F and 80.5°F (18°C and 27°C). The crew can adjust that temperature to whatever is comfortable. The Russian segment is a little warmer with temperatures between 68°F and 77°F (20°C and 25°C).[3]

STATION SUPPORT LAPTOPS

There are about 20 Station Support Computers (SSC) scattered throughout the modules. These are normal laptops running on Windows computer programs. The crews use them to look at their schedules, check procedures, review stowage notes, send and receive email, make phone calls and manage their photos. The crew can use these computers for anything that isn't involved in running the space station. These laptops are not connected to the internet—just the onboard network.[4]

CREW SUPPORT LAPTOPS

The crew have a second laptop (CSL) that is kept in their personal crew quarters and it's how the crew access the internet while on the ISS. These laptops are kept on a separate network from the on-board network. They also allow the crew to connect to a computer remotely in Houston to access the internet.[5] It's as slow as dialup at times, but it's the only way to tweet or google things from space.

FIRST TWEET IN SPACE

The internet has been available on the ISS since January 2010. To mark the milestone, NASA astronaut TJ Creamer sent the first tweet from space: "Hello Twitterverse! We r now LIVE tweeting from the International Space Station – the 1st live tweet from Space! ☺ More soon, send your ?s."[6]

CALLS FROM THE SPACE STATION TO HOUSTON ARE LOCAL

When astronauts call home they often use Voice Over IP which means they make voice calls using an internet connection. Because they connect to computers in Houston to access the internet, and those computers connect to the local internet provider, their location shows up as Houston,[7] Texas with the zip code 77058.[8]

ASTRONAUT ACCIDENTLY CALLS 911 FROM SPACE

While trying to call some friends on Earth, an astronaut heard a strange voice come on the line and say "What's your emergency?"

The astronaut had accidently omitted one of the zeros in the phone number they were trying to connect with and ended up calling 911! [9]

ONE-WAY PHONES

The Voice Over IP system astronauts use to call home only works in one direction. This means they can call anyone, but no one can call them. [10]

LUGGAGE ALLOWANCE

When traveling to the International Space Station, each astronaut is allowed a Personal Preference Kit (PPK) that measures 5 in. by 8 in. by 2 in. (12.7 cm by 20.32 cm by 5.08 cm), which is roughly the size of a lunch box. The PPK has a weight limit of 3.3 lbs. (1.5 kg).

Space shuttle astronauts had the same size PPK bag, but had to limit their items to just 20 separate items with the same weight limit that exists for missions to the ISS. [11]

CREW CARE PACKAGES

Astronauts get care packages from their families as part of psychological support. Care packages can include things like books,

Space station crews receive care packages to keep their spirits up while away from their families. Photo courtesy of NASA. [12]

favorite condiments, food, clothes, gifts, letters, photos, religious supplies, holiday decorations, personal effects or other things that contribute to maintaining close ties with family and overall emotional wellbeing during their mission.[13]

OFFICIAL FLIGHT KITS

For mementos for family members, organizations and support teams, crews can have Official Flight Kits (OFK). They can pack things like crew patches and pins, small flags, medallions,[14] or small personal photos.[15]

Sleeping

SLEEP STATIONS

Each crew member has their own little "crew quarters" where they sleep and keep their personal belongings. It's about the size of a tiny closet or phonebooth. Inside each crew quarters is a sleeping bag, air vent, personal laptop, work laptop, lamp, flashlight, and space for their personal belongings. There's also a speaker so that if there's an emergency, the ISS commander can alert the crew. Only the ISS commander's crew quarters has an alarm that allows the commander to wake the rest of the crew in case of an emergency.[16]

EARPLUGS AND EYE MASKS

The space station isn't the quietest place in space with the constant sound of life support machines running. Also, some astronauts snore! So, astronauts usually use earplugs or headphones to listen to music to help them sleep. Eye masks are helpful to block out the light since the sun rises roughly every 90 minutes.[17]

SLEEPING BAGS

The astronauts have lightweight sleeping bags that zip up the middle and have openings for not only their head, but also for their arms. They can sleep with their arms out and floating out in front of them or tucked inside the bag. They attach their sleeping bags to the

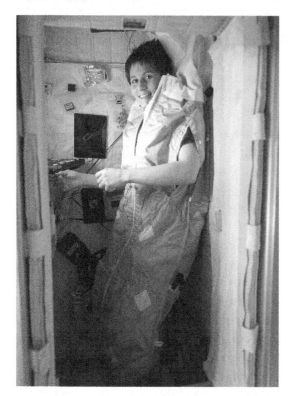

ESA astronaut Samantha Cristoforetti inside her sleeping bag inside her personal crew quarters on the ISS. Photo courtesy of NASA.[18]

wall so they don't move around while asleep. Some astronauts use Velcro and bungee cords to stay strapped in place.[19] The lightweight sleeping bags are often rolled up and out of the way during the day.

SLEEPING VERTICALLY

In microgravity, there is no difference between sleeping on the floor, the ceiling or the wall. But if you were to look at their crew quarters as a phone booth, then astronauts appear to sleep vertically within their crew quarters.[20]

SLEEP NEAR AN AIR VENT

While the astronauts can sleep most anywhere in the space station, what's important is that they sleep near an air vent. Their air only circulates with electric fans. Without ventilation, an astronaut could create a cloud or bubble of CO_2 as they exhaled. If they stayed in the same place, the astronaut would breathe in the carbon dioxide and slowly die. So, sleeping near a vent is critical![21]

HOW MUCH SLEEP DOES AN ASTROANUT NEED?

Astronauts have 8.5 hours of sleep time built into their schedules, but many have reported that they only need about 6 hours to feel fully rested. Researchers think this may have to do with the fact that their muscles don't have to work as hard as they do on Earth due to gravity. So, their bodies don't get tired as quickly.[22]

WINDOWS AND LIGHTS

The windows of the space station can be covered to help block out light during the 16 sunrises and sunsets, which is especially helpful when they are sleeping. The lights on the station can also be dimmed or switched off.

Personal Hygiene in Space

TOILETRY POUCH

Astronauts use a toiletry pouch about the size of a laptop case. It has pockets for their toothbrush, toothpaste, nail clippers, rinseless shampoo, deodorant, lotion and a camping towel. This towel comes in a pouch that the astronauts can use every second day to soap up and clean their skin. They can't wash towels or clothes in space, so they use these towels for a week and then get new ones that have been sent up in the cargo resupply spacecraft.

BATHING IN SPACE

While there was a shower on the space station Mir at one time, it was difficult to use. It was hard to keep water from floating off everywhere and potentially causing an electrical short. It also took a lot of time to vacuum up all of the water and then stow the shower. The shower experience itself wasn't as nice as you'd imagine since water floated everywhere instead of pouring down the body.

There are no showers on the International Space Station. Instead, astronauts use a bag of warm water, liquid soap and towels to bathe. They squirt a bit of water along their skin, then squirt liquid soap along their skin next to the water. Then they take their hands and rub the water and soap over their body to wash clean. They then use the towel to dry themselves off. Italian astronaut, Samantha Cristoforetti demonstrates this procedure here: https://youtu. be/7zhdanccUvs

WASHING YOUR HAIR

Astronauts with hair to wash use a bag of warm water, no-rinse shampoo, a towel and a mirror to watch what they're doing. They squirt a bit of the water into their hair and try to keep it there and not let water droplets float away. They then work it into their hair, add no-rinse shampoo, give it the best scrub they can, maybe add a bit more water then dry the excess water and shampoo from their hair. They then let their hair air dry as they go about the rest of their day. Watch astronaut Karen Nyberg wash her long hair in microgravity here: https://youtu.be/kOIj7AgonHM

BRUSHING YOUR TEETH

Astronauts brush their teeth in space with normal toothpaste, a normal toothbrush and a little bit of water from a water bag. But instead of spitting out their toothpaste into a sink, they either spit it out into a towel or they swallow it.[23]

CLIPPING YOUR FINGERNAILS

Clipping your nails so that they don't go floating off around the space station requires that you do it close to a return vent grid so that it's sucked into the grid filter. It's common courtesy to clean up after yourself, so astronauts use the vacuum and clean the filter afterwards.[24]

HAIRCUTS IN SPACE

When astronauts need a haircut, there are special hair clippers with

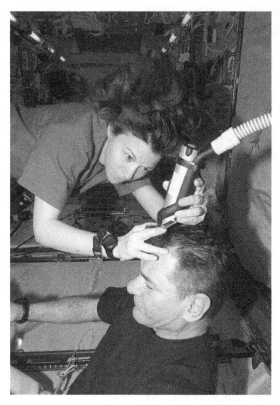

(*January 15, 2011*) *NASA astronaut Cady Coleman using special clippers to give ESA astronaut Paolo Nespoli a haircut onboard the ISS.* Photo courtesy of NASA.

a built-in vacuum device. This allows them to cut hair, but prevent it from floating off all over the station.

Some Russian cosmonauts consider getting a haircut in space unlucky. They will go their entire missions in space without cutting their hair because cosmonaut Sasha Kaleri was cutting his hair when the fire started on the space station Mir.[25]

TOILETS

There are two toilets on the ISS, one in the Zvezda service module on the Russian side and one in Node 3 on the American side.

In the fall of 2020, the ISS got a brand new, $23 million toilet with some major upgrades. One of the biggest enhancements is that it was made to better accommodate female astronauts. It also allows astronauts

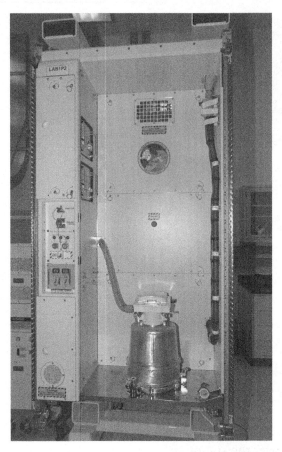

Older Russian-built toilet system that was delivered to the ISS in 2008. Photo courtesy of NASA.

New and improved toilet system for the ISS. Photo courtesy of NASA.

to go number one and number two at the same time if needed. This is the first space toilet to have this feature.[26] It's also automatic, which means the astronauts no longer have to worry about switching on the suction fan to help the waste go where it's supposed to go.

The $23 million is actually a two-for-one deal. If the one on the ISS works as designed, then a second one will travel to the Moon as part of NASA's upcoming Artemis 2 mission.[27]

Clothes in Space

PERSONAL ITEMS CHOSEN IN ADVANCE

Long before you fly into space, you sit down with the experts and pick from a list of space-safe items. You choose the clothes, tools, headlamps, notebooks, razors, sunglasses, toothpaste, deodorant and other personal items they will send up in advance for you.

TYPICAL CLOTHING SUPPLY

Astronauts have a limited supply of clothes that they use during a six-month mission onboard the ISS. While clothes worn on the space station don't normally get dirty, and can be worn multiple times before changing them, they can get sweaty and gross after being worn for a certain number of days.

This is the typical packing list for each astronaut:

a. 1 pair of running shoes for the treadmill
b. 1 pair of shoes for the bike
c. 1 pair of exercise shorts for every 3 days of exercise
d. 1 T-shirt for every 3 days of exercise
e. 1 work shirt for every 10 days
f. 1 T-shirt for under the work shirt for every 10 days
g. 1 pair of work pants or shorts for every 10 days
h. 1 pair of underwear for every 2 days
i. 1 pair of socks for every 2 days
j. 1 pair of pajamas for every 7 days
k. 2 sweaters
l. 2 pairs of Russian overalls (optional)[28]

Astronaut Cady Coleman with ziplock bags of clothes on the ISS. Photo courtesy of NASA.

EVERY TWO WEEKS

To keep things organized, clothes are split up into ziploc bags the astronauts call "bricks" that they get every two weeks. The bricks contain the clothes the astronaut will use for the next two weeks. For astronaut Samantha Cristoforetti, her brick contained "two cotton t-shirts, three pairs of socks, seven pairs of knickers (underwear), a camisole and two training outfits."[29]

NO LAUNDRY IN SPACE

In microgravity there is no practical way to do laundry. It would use too much valuable water. Once clothes start to smell, the astronauts pack them away to be sent back in the cargo spacecraft that will burn up in Earth's atmosphere.[30]

Exercising
NASA PERSONAL TRAINERS

The certified personal trainers who work with the astronauts are called ASCRs, which stands for the Astronaut Strength, Conditioning and Rehabilitation group. They work with the astronauts before, during and after their missions. Working with the astronauts while they are in space is especially important because astronauts can lose muscle mass and bone density. Astronauts can lose 1% to 1.5% of bone mass per month if they don't exercise to counteract the effects of microgravity.[31]

This can have a similar effect on the astronauts as people with osteoporosis. Much of what scientists have learned to help astronauts during space missions is helping treat and prevent osteoporosis for those of us back on Earth.

TAILOR-MADE DAILY WORKOUT PROGRAM

Each astronaut has a custom-made daily workout program that they perform while in space. The ASCRs track the astronaut's progress closely and will send updated plans when necessary. They also watch the astronaut's form and technique to make sure they're squatting properly and running on the treadmill with good form.[32]

TWO AND A HALF HOURS OF EXERCISE

Astronauts are required to exercise six days a week to counteract the loss of bone density and muscle mass. Each day, they are scheduled for 2.5 hours of exercise. The astronauts can split their time up and do it at different parts of the day if they choose, but they must get it done.[33] The 2.5 hours includes time to change clothes, set up the machines, exercise, recover from the workout and then clean up after the workout.[34]

TREADMILL ON THE WALL

All surfaces can be utilized in the space station, so the treadmill the astronauts use is on the wall! This special treadmill was designed so that astronauts can run on it without shaking the rest of the station,

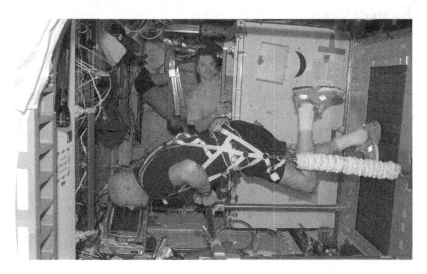

Astronauts & cosmonauts inside the Tranquility node on the ISS using both the COLBERT treadmill and in the very back, the weight lifting machine. ESA astronaut Andre Kuipers on the treadmill, cosmonaut Oleg Kononenko peeking out of a crew compartment and cosmonaut, Gennady Padalka in the very back using the ARED (Advanced Resistive Exercise Device.) Photo courtesy of NASA.

which could disturb or damage delicate experiments. The original treadmill was called TVIS, which stands for Treadmill with Vibration Isolation and Stabilization.

In 2009, an upgraded treadmill was sent to the space station and was named after the comedian Stephen Colbert, the former host of The Colbert Report. Colbert was the winning vote in an online poll to name what is now the Tranquility module. Instead of naming the module after Colbert, NASA decided to name the new and improved space treadmill the C.O.L.B.E.R.T. for Combined Operational Load Bearing External Resistance Treadmill and it's located in the Tranquility module.[35]

In order to run on the treadmill, astronauts use a harness that is anchored on both sides of the platform with two bungee cords. The harness is very similar to a backpacker's harness. Astronauts can adjust the loads from the shoulders to the hip. Astronauts normally run with a resistance between 70% to 90% of their full body weight.

WEIGHTLESS WEIGHT-LIFTING

The machine astronauts use for resistance training is called the Advanced Resistive Exercise Device (ARED). It allows the astronauts to perform the most common weight-lifting exercises with an adjustable load of up to 661 lbs (300 kg) for some types of exercises. It uses two vacuum cylinders to simulate the weight.[36] Astronauts can do squats, heel raises, shoulder presses, bench press, sit-ups, upright row, and bicep curls.[37]

EXERCISE BIKE WITH NO SEAT

The exercise bike, also called the Cycle Ergometer with Vibration Isolation and Stabilization, or CEVIS for short, has no seat. It doesn't

ESA astronaut Thomas Pesquet exercising on the CEVIS exercise bike inside the Destiny laboratory module on the ISS. Photo courtesy of NASA.

make sense to sit down while weightless. So, astronauts clip their bike shoes into the pedals, hold or push themselves down onto the handrails with their arms and pedal away.[38]

Weekends

SATURDAY CHORES

While on the ISS, the crew spends two to four hours every Saturday doing basic housekeeping chores to keep the place clean. This includes vacuuming, wiping down the station with disinfectant wipes and doing station maintenance that can't wait until Monday.

Vacuuming is a big part of the chores, and it can be a little tricky. The first challenge is finding a specific electrical outlet that's available. Almost all of the ISS electrical plugs are in use, and there are only certain outlets the vacuum can use, so astronauts have to refer to the official technical plug-in plan diagram to find an outlet.

The astronauts vacuum the filters and air vents where things like dust, crumbs, hair and dead skin can accumulate. Keeping the filters and vents clean helps keep the air flowing free.

The astronauts use disinfectant wipes to wipe down all the surfaces that are touched frequently or where flyaway food has landed. The floors, walls, ceilings, bathrooms, kitchen area, handrails and computer keyboards all get wiped down. [39]

 DID YOU KNOW?

Astronauts lose 0.1 ounces (3 grams) of skin per day while in space, which is double the amount humans lose on Earth.[40]

PERSONAL TIME

Weekends also give the crew time to video-conference with their families, catch up on personal emails, read, watch movies, enjoy the view of the Earth from the Cupola module, play games or just rest and get a break from their busy workweeks.

In-Flight Fun & Entertainment

MOVIES

The space station has a large digital library of movies and television shows[41] available as mp4 files that can be played on the laptops. They can even project onto one of the walls of the space station for the entire crew to enjoy![42]

Some of the movies you'll find onboard the ISS are titles you'd expect, like: *Alien, Star Wars* (new and old), *Star Trek* (new and old), *Gravity* and *2001: A Space Odyssey.*

Then there are several Hollywood classics like: *Casablanca, Citizen Kane, North by Northwest, Roman Holiday* and *To Kill A Mockingbird.*

To help with the holiday spirit, there are several holiday classics onboard like: *A Christmas Story, It's a Wonderful Life, It's the Great Pumpkin, Charlie Brown* and *White Christmas.*

For an easy night in to sit back and laugh, some of the comedies onboard include *Galaxy Quest, Ghostbusters, Groundhog Day, Men in Black, Oceans 13* and *The Princess Bride.*

On nights when the crew feels like singing (or watching other people do it), here are some of the Musicals onboard: *Chitty Chitty Bang Bang, Les Misérables, Moulin Rouge, Seven Brides for Seven Brothers, The Sound of Music* and *The Wizard of Oz.*

There's a good selection of Superhero movies from both Marvel and DC Comics.

And if the crew is feeling like kicking back and watching a romantic comedy, they can choose from titles like: *A Knight's Tale, Return to Me, Sleepless in Seattle, That Thing You Do!* and *The Wedding Singer.*

TV SHOWS

There's a wide variety of television shows onboard as well. There's everything from action and crime to comedy-dramas and science. You'll find seasons of *24* (Seasons 1-8), *Firefly, Friends, MythBusters* (Seasons 1-7), *Seinfeld* (Seasons 1-3), and *Sherlock* (Seasons 1-3).[43]

The ground support team will sometimes uplink NBC Nightly News as well as livestream CNN or ESPN to keep the crew up to date on what's happening in the world below.[44]

MUSIC

While the station has a general collection of music, many astronauts will bring their personal iPods with their own playlists to listen to and share with the others. Each astronaut has a support team member who can uplink new music for them to keep things fresh.[45]

BOOKS

The ISS has few physical books onboard, since there isn't much room for them. Instead, most of the books are in digital form. The station has classics like A Tale of Two Cities and 20,000 Leagues Under the Sea. There are thrillers like Dan Brown's Angels and Demons and The DaVinci Code, as well as David McCullough's 1776. Some astronauts bring their own books or have their support team uplink books for them. Scott Kelly, who spent nearly a year in space, brought Endurance: Shackleton's Incredible Voyage by Alfred Lansing with him.[46]

LEGOS IN SPACE

Building Lego models can be a challenge on Earth, but can you imagine what it would be like when pieces float while in space? On the plus side, you don't have to worry about stepping on them! Japanese astronaut Satoshi Furukawa brought several Lego sets with him to build during his mission. He managed to complete Lego models of the ISS, the Mars rovers and the Hubble Space Telescope.[47]

MUSICAL INSTRUMENTS

Several musical instruments have flown to the ISS. Some were left behind by previous crews. In 2001, NASA psychiatrists sent up a guitar to stay permanently, since they felt it was good for mental health.[48] A few other instruments found on the space station include a ukulele and an electric piano.[49]

SPACE CRAFTS

While in space and away from her young son, NASA astronaut Karen Nyberg used scraps of food-packaging liners and a t-shirt to make a stuffed dinosaur toy. Her son loves dinosaurs and she would send

Stuffed dinosaur made from items around the ISS by NASA astronaut Karen Nyberg. Photo courtesy of NASA.

him photos of her special space-dinosaur while on the International Space Station.[50]

Games Played in Space

To help with boredom, burnout and their mental health, astronauts are encouraged to play games in their spare time while in space. Not all games work in microgravity, but astronauts are clever and have come up with some pretty interesting ways to play their favorite games.

CHESS

NASA astronaut Gregory Chamitoff brought an ultra-lightweight chessboard with hollow plastic pieces with Velcro bases that attached to the Velcro board. Not only did crewmates play chess with each other, they played an "interplanetary space game" against those of

Astronaut Gregory Chamitoff plays chess in Node 2 on the International Space Station. Photo courtesy of NASA.

us on Earth who suggested countermoves in a game facilitated by the United States Chess Federation.[51]

SCRABBLE

A modified Scrabble travel board with Velcro attached to the board and each individual letter makes it possible to play one of the most popular word games.

MODIFIED DARTS

Commander Chris Hadfield developed space darts using items he found around the space station. No sharp objects could be used, so instead he used a heavy camera battery for a nose, two zip-ties for a shaft and notepaper for fletching. It sounds clunky, but in microgravity, these space darts fly gracefully across the spacecraft cabins.[52]

BASKETBALL

A small basketball and hoop have even found their way to the International Space Station for astronauts who love a friendly game of basketball. Dunk away!

During his downtime, astronaut Frank L. Culbertson, Jr. plays basketball in the Unity node on the International Space Station. Photo courtesy of NASA.

Holidays

EIGHT HOLIDAYS A YEAR

The crew's schedule on the ISS can accommodate eight holidays per year. Before their six months onboard, the crew will get together to decide which four holidays to observe during their mission. These holidays can include ones from America, Russia, Europe, Japan and Canada.[53]

Sharing international traditions with each other is one of the most cherished memories for the crews.

SPECIAL MEALS AND CALLING HOME

For holidays, the international crews will share a special meal together and then call home to talk to friends, family and other loved ones.

THANKSGIVING

Three weeks after the first crew arrived onboard the International Space Station on November 2, 2000, they celebrated their first Thanksgiving. Since then, Thanksgiving has been celebrated at the space station every November. The international crews gather to share a meal.

NASA sends up a meal that is as close to a traditional Thanksgiving feast you could get while in space. This includes packages of smoked turkey, ham, mashed potatoes, macaroni and cheese, candied yams, green beans and mushrooms, cornbread dressing and cranapple dessert or blueberry-cherry cobbler.[54]

TWO CHRISTMASES ON THE ISS

The crews onboard the ISS celebrate Christmas two different times. Most astronauts celebrate on December 25th. The Russians celebrate the Orthodox Christmas, which falls on January 7th.

There's a box of Christmas decorations on the ISS that crews use to make the place feel more festive around the holidays. Some of the decorations include plastic strings of lights, Santa hats, Christmas stockings and a Christmas tree just a little over one foot tall.[55]

HOLIDAY SHOPPING A YEAR IN ADVANCE

Clothes and other personal items are often sent to the space station months before the crew actually arrive onboard. If you wanted to share gifts with your crewmates or get matching festive pajamas, you'd have to think a year or more in advance to make sure you purchase, pack and get them "shipped" in time.[56]

NEW YEAR'S EVE

On the space station, New Year's Eve is a bigger holiday than Christmas because it's celebrated by all nations on the same day.[57] But not always at the same time of day! Because the clocks on the space station are set to UTC time, the first New Year in Moscow is celebrated when the clocks say 9 p.m. When the ISS clocks say 11 p.m., the crew celebrates the arrival of the New Year on the European continent. Then when

Expedition 16 crew celebrating Christmas onboard the ISS. Left to Right: cosmonaut Yuri I. Malenchenko, astronaut Peggy A. Whitson, and astronaut Daniel Tani. Photo courtesy of NASA.

the clocks read midnight on the station, the crew celebrates with cheers, singing and silly dances.[58]

Watching the 1976 Soviet romantic comedy movie *The Irony of Fate* on New Year's Eve is a big tradition in Russia and is also practiced onboard the space station.

HALLOWEEN

While there may not be any trick-or-treaters visiting the International Space Station, crewmembers still enjoy dressing up and getting into the Halloween spirit. Over the years, crews have come up with some creative costumes and have even used fresh oranges brought up by resupply vehicles as makeshift jack-o'-lanterns. Costumes have included Superman, Wolverine, Spiderman, minions from Despicable Me, Waldo from Where's Waldo?, a pirate, a mad scientist and other clever costumes.[59]

*Celebrating Halloween on the ISS.
Above: The Expedition 53 crew all dressed
up. NASA astronaut Nicole P. Stott's jack-o'-
lantern made from an orange. Left: Italian
Space Agency astronaut Luca S. Parmitano
as Superman.* Photos courtesy of NASA.

NOTES

1. "Robert Frost's Answer to Does ISS Observe Daylight Saving Time? – Quora," Quora, accessed May 30, 2021, https://qr.ae/pGNPhq.

2. Samantha Cristoforetti, *Diary of an Apprentice Astronaut*, trans. Jill Foulston (Penguin, 2020), 302, Kindle.

3. "The Average Temperature Aboard The Space Station," The Space Store, August 1, 2018, https://thespacestore.com/blogs/blog/the-average-temperature-aboard-the-space-station.

4. Cristoforetti, *Diary of an Apprentice Astronaut*, 266.

5. *Where Do Astronauts Sleep?*, YouTube (European Space Agency, 2015), https://youtu.be/YlUzva6lRQQ.

6. Tim Peake, *Ask an Astronaut: My Guide to Life in Space* (Little Brown and Company, 2017), 131.

7. Cristoforetti, *Diary of an Apprentice Astronaut*, 272.

8. "Robert Frost's Answer to What Would Happen If You Allow a Site to Access Your Current Location While Aboard the ISS? – Quora," Quora, accessed May 30, 2021, https://qr.ae/pGNPV9.

9. Cristoforetti, *Diary of an Apprentice Astronaut*, 272.

10. Cristoforetti, *Diary of an Apprentice Astronaut*, 251.

11. Brian Dunbar, "The Personal Preference Kit: What Astronauts Take With Them To Space," ed. Thalia Patrinos, NASA (NASA, November 18, 2020), https://www.nasa.gov/feature/the-personal-preference-kit-what-astronauts-take-with-them-to-space.

12. Brian Dunbar, "Behavioral Health," ed. Robert Lewis, NASA, last modified August 12, 2021, https://www.nasa.gov/content/behavioral-health.

13. Cristoforetti, *Diary of an Apprentice Astronaut*, 379.

14. "Official Flight Kit, STS-132," NASA, accessed May 30, 2021, https://www.nasa.gov/pdf/450571main_132_flight_kit.pdf.

15. "Robert Frost's Answer to What Is the Baggage Allowance for Astronauts/Cosmonauts? – Quora," Quora, accessed May 30, 2021, https://qr.ae/pGN4ah.

16. Peake, *Ask an Astronaut*, 99.

17. Terry Virts, *How to Astronaut: An Insider's Guide to Leaving Planet Earth* (New York, Workman Publishing, 2020), 116.

18. "Cristoforetti in Crew quarters," NASA, December 6, 2015, photograph, https://images.nasa.gov/details-iss042e023422.

19. NASA, STEMonstrations: *Sleep Science*, December 13, 2018, video, NASA, https://images.nasa.gov/details-jsc2018m000902-STEMonstrations_Sleep_Science_MP4.

20. "Sleeping in Space," CSA (Canadian Space Agency, August 22, 2019), https://www.asc-csa.gc.ca/eng/astronauts/living-in-space/sleeping-in-space.asp.

21. Virts, *How to Astronaut*, 13.

22. CSA, "Sleeping in Space."

23. *How Do Astronauts Brush Their Teeth in Space?*, YouTube (Science, 2020), https://youtu.be/jNqPCJOZLGo.

24. *Doing Your Nails and Hair in Space - Astronaut Samantha Cristoforetti's Tips: Video*, YouTube (ESA, 2015), https://youtu.be/PrqcwH8LhDU.

25. Scott Kelly, *Endurance: A Year in Space, A Lifetime of Discovery* (New York: Alfred A. Knopf, 2017), 101.

26. Brian Dunbar, "Boldly Go! NASA's New Space Toilet," ed. Darcy Elburn, NASA (NASA, September 24, 2020), https://www.nasa.gov/feature/boldly-go-nasa-s-new-space-toilet-offers-more-comfort-improved-efficiency-for-deep-space/.

27. Amy Thompson, "NASA Just Sent a New $23 Million Space Toilet to the International Space Station," Smithsonian.com (Smithsonian Institution, October 9, 2020), https://www.smithsonianmag.com/science-nature/nasa-just-sent-new-23-million-space-toilet-international-space-station-180976037/.

28. "Robert Frost's Answer to What Is the Typical Clothing Inventory of an Astronaut Spending 6 Months on the ISS? – Quora," Quora, accessed May 30, 2021, https://qr.ae/pGGIQd.

29. Cristoforetti, *Diary of an Apprentice Astronaut*, 322.

30. "Personal Hygiene in Space," CSA (Canadian Space Agency, August 26, 2019), https://www.asc-csa.gc.ca/eng/astronauts/living-in-space/personal-hygiene-in-space.asp.

31. Virts, *How to Astronaut*, 51-52.

32. Virts, *How to Astronaut*, 52.

33. Cristoforetti, *Diary of an Apprentice Astronaut*, 267.

34. Gary Jordan, "Ep 33: The Zero-G Workout," Houston, We Have a Podcast (NASA, February 21, 2018), https://www.nasa.gov/johnson/HWHAP/the-zero-g-workout.

35. "NASA Names Space Module for Moon Base, Not Colbert," collectSPACE.com, April 14, 2009, http://www.collectspace.com/news/news-041409a.html.

36. Cristoforetti, *Diary of an Apprentice Astronaut*, 267.

37. Peake, *Ask an Astronaut*, 133.

38. Cristoforetti, *Diary of an Apprentice Astronaut*, 261-262.

39. Virts, *How to Astronaut*, 130.

40. "Weightless Washcloths and Floating Showers," ESA (European Space Agency, April 19, 2006), https://www.esa.int/Science_Exploration/Human_and_Robotic_Exploration/Business/Weightless_washcloths_and_floating_showers.

41. Matt Novak, "The Complete List of Movies and TV Shows On Board the International Space Station," Gizmodo, July 5, 2016, https://paleofuture.gizmodo.com/the-complete-list-of-movies-and-tv-shows-on-the-interna-1782918945.

42. NASA, "NASA List of books, movies, television shows, and music maintained on the International Space Station (ISS) for recreational/off-duty consumption," Governmentattic.org, April 29, 2008, https://www.governmentattic.org/docs/ISS_Media_2008.pdf.

43. Government Attic, "NASA List of books, movies, television shows and music."

44. Virts, *How to Astronaut*, 176.

45. Virts, *How to Astronaut*, 175.

46. Kelly, *Endurance*, 77.

47. Amanda Wills, "7 Oddball Things Found on the Space Station," Mashable (Mashable, July 7, 2013), https://mashable.com/2013/07/07/odd-things-space-station/.

48. Mary von Aue, "Astronaut Explains the Psychological Reason a Guitar Is on the ISS," Inverse (Inverse, June 3, 2018), https://www.inverse.com/article/45503-astronaut-explains-the-psychological-reason-a-guitar-is-on-the-iss.

49. Richard Hollingham, "Thirteen Space Music Firsts," BBC Future (BBC, November 18, 2018), https://www.bbc.com/future/article/20130429-thirteen-space-music-firsts.

50. Mark Garcia, "Stuffed Dinosaur Toy," NASA, last modified September 30, 2013, https://www.nasa.gov/content/stuffed-dinosaur-toy.

51. Leanne Prain, "Zero-Gravity Games: How Astronauts Play in Space," WorksThatWork.com, accessed April 21, 2022, https://worksthatwork.com/9/zero-gravity-games-how-astronauts-play-in-space.

52. Watch Commander Hadfield play a game of space darts and show off his space-Scrabble board on YouTube: https://www.youtube.com/watch?v=cobJzLQqUmo

53. "Robert Frost's Answer to On Thanksgiving, Does Mission Control Operate at Full Capacity or Reduced Staff since the ISS Won't Be Doing Any Science or Maintenance That Day? - Quora," Quora, accessed May 30, 2021, https://qr.ae/pGN3G3.

54. Brian Dunbar, "Space Station 20th: Thanksgiving Celebrations in Space," ed. Kelli Mars, NASA (NASA, last modified November 23, 2020), https://www.nasa.gov/feature/space-station-20th-thanksgiving-celebrations-in-space.

55. Wills, "Found on the Space Station."

56. Ashley Strickland, "This Is How Astronauts Celebrate Christmas and Other Holidays in Space," CNN (Cable News Network, December 25, 2020), https://www.cnn.com/2020/12/25/world/nasa-astronauts-christmas-space-scn-trnd/index.html.

57. Kelly, *Endurance*, 339.

58. Cristoforetti, *Diary of an Apprentice Astronaut*, 280, 282.

59. John Uri, "Space Station 20th: Halloween on the ISS," ed. Kelli Mars, NASA (NASA, last modified November 2, 2020), https://www.nasa.gov/feature/space-station-20th-halloween-on-iss.

WORKING ON THE ISS

A Day in the Life of an ISS Crew Member

AN AVERAGE DAY ON THE ISS

Astronauts schedules are planned down to five-minute increments by the Ops Planner team in Mission Control. Their schedules are accessed on the computers scattered throughout the space station. Work tasks, downtime, sleep, meals, chores, experiments, exercise and everything else is all scheduled.

An average 24-hour day consists of 8.5 hours for sleeping, 6.5 hours for work, 2.5 hours to exercise, 1 hour for lunch, 2.5 hours of downtime in the evening for dinner and relaxing and the rest of the time is used for work prep and touching base with Mission Control centers around the world.

Astronauts are scheduled to eat three meals a day: breakfast, lunch and dinner. The crews work 5.5 days a week with 1.5 days off over the weekend.

STANDARD CREW WORKDAY SCHEDULE

06:00 AM – Crew wake-up. Dress, eat breakfast, brush teeth and check messages uplinked overnight.

07:30 AM – Morning Daily Planning Conference (DPC). Astronauts and Cosmonauts sync up with Mission Control Centers in Houston, Texas; Huntsville, Alabama; Munich, Germany; Tsukuba, Japan; and Moscow, Russia, before starting their day.

07:55 AM – Work prep, review procedures and gather supplies to support the day's activities.

08:15 AM – Scheduled work tasks begin, including things like science experiments, preventative and corrective maintenance, prepping for visiting spacecrafts, stowage operations, environment sampling (acoustics, surfaces, water), public affairs events, other medical tasks and mandatory daily 2.5 hours of exercise.

01:00 PM – Lunch

02:00 PM – More scheduled work tasks (see above).

06:15 PM - Evening work prep, review procedures and timeline for next day.

07:05 PM – Evening DPC. Discuss any comments or questions about their tasks and experiments that day. If required, a brief chat about any changes for tomorrow's schedule.

07:30 PM - Dinner, relax, email, organize images for downlink, watch a movie, enjoy the view of Earth.

09:30 PM – Time to sleep (8.5 hours)[1]

SPACE-TO-GROUND COMMUNICATIONS

Because it's the *International* Space Station, all conversations are interpreted in real-time into English, Russian, German, Japanese and any other languages needed. Then they are sent to other Mission Control centers around the world.[2]

COMMUNICATION WITH MISSION CONTROL

The lines of communication between the ISS and Mission Control in Houston, Texas, are almost constant due to the satellites that relay information, no matter where the station is.

That's not the case for Mission Control in Russia. During the early Soviet Union space missions, cosmonauts were only able to communicate with their Mission Control or TsUP, pronounced like "soup," when they passed over large dish antennas within the Soviet Union. That tradition of not being in constant communication with the crew is still how it works, so TsUP has scheduled windows of communications with the crew.[3]

LIVING IN A FISHBOWL

Every day after the Daily Planning Conference (DPC) meeting in the morning, the wide-angle cameras onboard the space station begin to transmit to Earth. There are cameras in the Lab; Nodes 1, 2 and 3;

JEM and in the background of Columbus. The areas in in Nodes 2 and 3 are for living, hygiene and exercise so the cameras here are often turned to the wall to give some privacy to the crew.[4]

The live video from the International Space Station that includes views of the crew when they're on duty, as well as audio conversations between the crew and Mission Control and views of Earth from space at other times can be viewed at: https://www.nasa.gov/multimedia/nasatv/iss_ustream.html

NO WEEKEND STREAMING
The weekends are a time when the astronauts can relax and are given more privacy. The onboard cameras are set to not download the live video during this time.[5]

NO CAMERAS IN RUSSIAN SEGMENT
In the Russian segment, there aren't cameras transmitting images to control centers or streamed live for the world to see.[6]

A LIVE VIEW OF EARTH
A camera mounted on the outside of the ISS streams live video footage showing Earth below as the ISS flies by at between 17,150 mph to 17,500 mph (27,600 kph to 28,200 kph). This works out to about 5 miles per second (8 km per second).

Here's where you can see the view of Earth as seen from the International Space Station: https://www.asc-csa.gc.ca/eng/iss/watch-live.asp

PHOTOS OF THE EARTH
NASA shares all of the photos that astronauts take of Earth for educational and scientific research. Astronauts are trained to take high quality photos from space, but also are trained to take photos of scientific observation—from events like volcano eruptions and hurricanes to natural wonders like coral reefs and icebergs, or to document human impacts on Earth like city growth and agricultural expansion.[7]

Want to see the best and most complete collection of photographs taken of the Earth since 1961? Visit NASA's database at: https://eol. jsc.nasa.gov/

JOBS ON THE ISS

There are three different levels of qualification for astronauts onboard the International Space Station: User, Operator, and Specialist. Each of these roles have certain tasks and responsibilities and there is specific training for each role.

Astronaut Samantha Cristoforetti explains the roles by comparing them to using a washing machine. A user knows how do the laundry. An operator understands all the functions and knows what it looks like when something is acting up or about to break. A specialist can take the machine apart and put it back together.[8]

EXPERIMENTS AND RESEARCH

Since the ISS has been occupied, astronauts have conducted over 3,000 scientific and educational investigations for 108 countries. The research and experiments onboard help us explore deeper into space, but also benefit us back on Earth.

Experiments range from recycling in space to studying ailments like cancer and Parkinson's disease. Research is also done on Earth in several areas, including space science, physical science, human research, education activities, technology development and biology and biotechnology.

SPACE STATION MAINTENANCE

Crews perform maintenance on parts of the ISS to keep things in working order. But, since the space station is never going to return to Earth, if something breaks while in space, it's up to the astronauts and cosmonauts to fix it. Astronaut training programs include lessons on electronics repair and a deep understanding of the machinery onboard and outside the station.

Astronauts must know how to fix the toilets and life support systems, update the computer equipment, repair torn solar panels, fix potential ammonia and module pressure leaks, and much more. Many spacewalks are all about maintenance or repairs.

Resupply Vehicles

The only thing 100% homemade onboard the International Space Station is electricity from its eight massive solar panels. Other than that, everything must be recycled or delivered from Earth. This includes food, fuel, water, oxygen, clothes, spare equipment and care packages.[9]

SPECIAL DELIVERY LAUNCH WINDOWS

Cargo resupply ships can only arrive or depart on certain days. Scheduling launch windows can sometimes be difficult. There can't be any deliveries on spacewalk days or when crews are arriving or headed home to Earth. There are also a few weeks per year where the sun shines its light so directly on the station that it becomes overheated. So those weeks are out.[10]

PACKED WITH CARE

Once a good launch window has been found, the spacecraft needs to be packed. Typical cargo items include water, fuel, clothes, science experiments (which sometimes include live mice!), food, spare parts and crew care packages.

Often, if there is extra space, ground crews will pack a few fresh fruits and vegetables. Since most of the food astronauts eat is prepackaged, fresh food is a special treat. When a freezer for experiments was sent up, it was packed with real ice cream as a treat for the crew.

LAUNCH DELAYS

When packing items like clothes and parts, it doesn't matter as much if the launch is delayed because those can be packed months in advance. But for live mice and plants, delays can cause problems. There is a limited window in which they can be loaded because there's only a certain amount of time they can be inside the vehicle. If the launch is delayed, those live organisms have to be unloaded and a new "crew" loaded closer to the new launch date.

It's normal to have a crew of 40 mice headed to the space station, but there's a backup population of 1,000 mice ready to go in case they're needed. This allows for enough mice to be ready for the experiments in space, but also allows for a control group that scientists study on Earth.[11]

SAME-DAY DELIVERY OR TWO-DAY SHIPPING?

Each resupply cargo ship takes a different route and the shipping time can vary. The Russian Progress cargo ships can fly themselves all the way to docking within a few hours from launch.

Other vehicles take a little longer—usually a few days—to line up and fly alongside the ISS. The Japanese HTV (4 to 7 days)[12], SpaceX Dragon (1 to 2 days)[13] and Northrop Grumman Cygnus (2 days)[14] all fly up to a point about 30 feet (9 meters) below the station. They then need to reach a speed of at least 17,500 mph (27,600 kph) to match the rate of the ISS before they can be grabbed.

Astronauts use the station's robotic arm, the Canadarm2, while looking out from the seven-windowed Cupola module and manually grab the cargo ship. Once the crew has grabbed the vehicle, Mission Control in Houston takes control of the robotic arm and moves it to a free docking port. It's berthed there or attached firmly to the ISS with electrically driven bolts.[15]

UNPACKING CARGO SHIPS

Unpacking cargo ships is a tedious and stressful job. Astronauts need to make sure that the equipment is moved out in a certain order and put exactly where it needs to go—so it doesn't get lost. It can take several weeks to fully unpack a cargo ship!

Everything that is unpacked goes into labeled fabric bags with bar codes, and text that describes what's inside. Every item belongs in a particular place in a specific module, and needs to be placed in a specific bag or locker on a specific wall, floor or ceiling of that module.

More than 6,400 pounds (2,900 kg) of science investigations and cargo packed and ready to send to the ISS on the SpaceX CRS-21 Cargo resupply mission. Photo courtesy of NASA.

Usually the crew care packages, fresh food, ice cream and mice are easily accessible and are the first to be unloaded.[16]

RETURNING CARGO SHIPS

There are two types of cargo ships, each with specific uses. Single-use cargo ships returning to Earth become a type of garbage truck. They are packed with garbage, dirty clothes and towels, lightweight packing material, solid-waste containers and anything else no longer needed by the crew. The crew uses the Canadarm2 robotic arm to release the single-use cargo ship, sending it to safely burn up like a shooting star as it re-enters Earth's atmosphere. Make a wish!

Most of the cargo ships are currently single-use. SpaceX sends up the only reusable cargo vehicle, called the Cargo Dragon. This cargo ship can send back experiments, biomedical samples, equipment that can be refurbished and reused and any personal items that a crew member wants returned to Earth.[17] The Cargo Dragon takes four to nine hours to return to Earth under a parachute-assisted splashdown. Additional reusable cargo ships are in the making.[18]

NOTES

1. "Chris Buckley's Answer to What's the Typical Daily Schedule in the International Space Station? – Quora," Quora, accessed May 30, 2021, https://qr.ae/pGGHgs.

2. Samantha Cristoforetti, *Diary of an Apprentice Astronaut*, trans. Jill Foulston (Penguin, 2020), 242, Kindle.

3. Chris Hadfield, "Comms: Mission Control Evolution and Operations," MasterClass (MasterClass), accessed May 30, 2021, https://www.masterclass.com/classes/chris-hadfield-teaches-space-exploration/chapters/comms-mission-control-evolution-and-operations.

4. Cristoforetti, *Diary of an Apprentice Astronaut*, 263.

5. Alyssa Newcomb, "Astronauts Have to Vacuum and 4 Other Things We Learned From Samantha Cristoforetti," ABC News (ABC News Network, December 1, 2014), https://abcnews.go.com/Technology/astronauts-vacuum-things-learned-samantha-cristoforetti/story?id=27287053.

6. Cristoforetti, *Diary of an Apprentice Astronaut*, 321.

7. "Crew Earth Observations," Space Station Research Explorer on NASA.gov (NASA), accessed May 30, 2021, https://www.nasa.gov/mission_pages/station/research/experiments/explorer/Investigation.html#id=84.

8. Samantha Cristoforetti, *Diary of an Apprentice Astronaut*, trans. Jill Foulston (Penguin, 2020), 141, Kindle.

9. Terry Virts, *How to Astronaut: An Insider's Guide to Leaving Planet Earth* (New York, Workman Publishing, 2020), 170.

10. Virts, *How to Astronaut*, 170.

11. Virts, *How to Astronaut*, 170-171.

12. Wikipedia, s.v. "H-II Transfer Vehicle," last modified May 8, 2021, https://en.wikipedia.org/wiki/H-II_Transfer_Vehicle.

13. Wikipedia, s.v. "SpaceX CRS-20," last modified May 13, 2021, https://en.wikipedia.org/wiki/SpaceX_CRS-20.

14. Wikipedia, s.v. "Cygnus NG-11," last modified May 24, 2021, https://en.wikipedia.org/wiki/Cygnus_NG-11.

15. Virts, *How to Astronaut*, 170-171.

16. Scott Kelly, *Endurance: A Year in Space, A Lifetime of Discovery* (New York: Alfred A. Knopf, 2017), 99.

17. Virts, *How to Astronaut*, 173.

18. Hanneke Weitering, "SpaceX's Upgraded Cargo Dragon Supply Ship Makes 1st Atlantic Splashdown," Space.com, January 14, 2021, https://www.space.com/spacex-upgraded-dragon-crs-21-atlantic-splashdown.

SPACEWALKS

Anytime an astronaut leaves the safety of their space vehicle while in space, it's considered a spacewalk. This is also known as an EVA, which stands for an extravehicular activity. It's also one of the first things we picture when we think of astronauts, even though not every astronaut gets to spacewalk while they are in space. Astronauts have performed spacewalks on the Moon, in deep space while on their way back from the Moon and outside different spacecrafts and space stations.

Spacewalk Firsts

THE FIRST HUMAN TO SPACEWALK

Cosmonaut Alexei Leonov became the first human to venture outside his Voskhod spacecraft into the blackness of space on March 18, 1965. During his spacewalk, Leonov filmed the Earth below and reported that "The Earth is absolutely round." He was tethered to the Voskhod with a cord 16 feet (5 meters) long. His spacewalk lasted 12 minutes and 9 seconds. His suit swelled up due to the pressure, but Leonov was able to release the suit's pressure and reenter the airlock.

Part of the reason Leonov was chosen as the first man to spacewalk is that he was a talented artist. He brought colored pencils and paper on the spacecraft and drew his view of the sunrise over Earth. Not only was he the first to spacewalk, Leonov was also the first to draw in space.[1]

A heart-shaped crater on the far side of the Moon is named after him. It's called the Leonov Crater.[2]

THE FIRST AMERICAN TO SPACEWALK

Just a few months after Alexei Leonov made his historic spacewalk, American astronaut Ed White spent about 20 minutes on a spacewalk on June 3, 1965. His tether was 23 feet (7 meters) long. To maneuver in

Astronaut Ed White became the first American astronaut to spacewalk on June 3, 1965. Photo courtesy of NASA.

space during his EVA, White used a "zip gun," which is an oxygen-jet gun also known as the Hand-Held Maneuvering Unit.[3]

While on that spacewalk, a glove floated out of the Gemini 4 airlock and became one of the first items of space debris. Ed White is most famously known for being the first American to perform a spacewalk, but he was also one of the three astronauts who tragically died in the Apollo 1 fire.

THE FIRST WOMAN TO SPACEWALK

On her second space mission, Russian cosmonaut Svetlana Savitskaya became the first woman to walk in space. She already held the record for being the second woman in space and the first woman to fly to space twice. Her spacewalk lasted 3 hours and 35 minutes and she and her co-cosmonaut welded and cut medals in space. She is the only Russian female cosmonaut to have performed a spacewalk.[4]

THE FIRST UNTETHERED SPACEWALK

In February of 1984, American astronaut Bruce McCandless II became the first to use the Manned Maneuvering Unit (MMU), which allowed him to float untethered more than 300 feet (91 meters) from the *Challenger* space shuttle.[5] Over the two days, he and astronaut Robert Stewart performed several untethered spacewalks using the MMU. Together, those spacewalks lasted a total of 5 hours and 10 minutes.[6]

McCandless waited almost 18 years before going into space. During that time, he served as CAPCOM (Capsule Communicator) for Apollo 11, Apollo 14, Skylab 3 and Skylab 4. He also worked on the development of the MMU. It was a long wait, but after that accomplishment I'm sure he would say it was worth it!

SPACEWALKS ARE RARE

We like to think that spacewalks happen all the time, but in reality, they don't. Spacewalks are dangerous. A spacewalk will only happen if the procedure can't be done robotically and needs human hands and eyes on it. Not every astronaut or cosmonaut who goes into space goes on a spacewalk.

Sometimes this is due to the size of available spacesuits, as was the case for Samantha Cristoforetti. She had trained hundreds of hours for a spacewalk, but there wasn't a spacesuit that fit her on the ISS, so she wasn't able to go. There were other reasons, but the size of the available suits was a large part of it.[7]

Since Alexei Leonov performed the first spacewalk in 1965, just over 230 people have worn a spacesuit and spacewalked—including the moonwalkers.[8] That means that of the 593 people who have been to space as of 2022, less than half have had the opportunity to spacewalk. However, some have had the opportunity to spacewalk multiple times.

Training for Spacewalks

After Alexei Leonov's near-fatal spacewalk, astronauts have trained underwater to be better prepared for spacewalking in space.

EARLY NASA ASTRONAUTS TRAINED IN THE CARIBBEAN

Before there was a pool built specifically to be used for spacewalk training, early astronauts trained and practiced for spacewalks in the Caribbean.[9]

TRAINING IN ONE OF THE BIGGEST POOLS IN THE WORLD

In the US, EVA training is done at the Sonny Carter Training Facility in Houston, Texas, near the Johnson Space Center. Sonny Carter was an astronaut who died in an airplane accident, and the facility was named in his honor. This facility is also called the Neutral Buoyancy Lab, or NBL for short.

The NBL pool is 202 feet (62 m) long, 102 feet (31 m) wide, and 40 feet (12 m) deep. Of those 40 feet, 20 are above ground level and 20 are below ground level. It holds 6.2 million gallons (23 million liters) of water.[10]

To put that into perspective, the ISS is 357 feet (108.8 m) long by 240 feet (73 m) wide, so only large models of certain ISS modules are in the pool. The space shuttle was 122.2 feet (37 m) long and 56.67 feet (17 m) high, with a wingspan of 78.06 feet (23.7 m).[11]

OTHER NEUTRAL BUOYANCY POOLS

In Star City, outside of Moscow, cosmonauts train at the Hydrolab, which was built in 1980. ESA astronauts train in Houston, but also have their own tank at the European Astronaut Centre in Germany. Japanese astronauts have a tank at the Tsukuba Space Center outside of Tokyo. Chinese astronauts train in Beijing at the Chinese Astronaut Research Training Center.[12]

FULL-SCALE REPLICAS IN THE POOL

Astronauts spend hundreds and hundreds of hours training underwater in the NBL in their spacesuits using full-scale replicas of the different things they'll encounter while spacewalking. When the space shuttle was in use, there was a huge replica of a section of the space shuttle underwater that they would practice on. There was even a replica of the Hubble Telescope, which received repairs while astronauts were on spacewalks.

A glimpse of what astronauts see and train on underwater in the NBL. *Photograph by Mark Sowa.* Photo courtesy of NASA.

Whatever astronauts will work on, there's an accurate mockup of it so they will be as prepared as possible to do it in space. These days, astronauts work on replicas of huge sections and full-size mockups of modules of the International Space Station and the Canadarm2.[13]

I FEEL SICK

Some astronauts get sick in the pool as soon as they go underwater because the view behind their helmet changes to a weird, magnified view. They are warned about this phenomenon and instructed to say something as quickly as possible if they do feel sick so that they can be raised up out of the water and receive help taking their helmets off in case they vomit.[14]

BECOMING NEUTRALLY BUOYANT

To make the experience as close to being weightless in space as possible, two safety divers take astronauts down to the bottom of the pool and place weights around their ankles, waist, and other parts of the suit. These weights create neutral buoyancy. This means the astronauts are perfectly motionless in the water, not floating up and not floating down. While it's not exactly like being weightless, it's the best method we have on Earth to train astronauts.[15]

WHICH WAY IS NORTH?

To keep everyone oriented in the pool, large compass heading letters N, S, E, and W are painted on the walls of the pool.

LESSON ONE: USING THE AIRLOCK

Once the astronauts have been weighted properly, they are shoved into a tiny airlock with their partner to begin training on the day's task. The airlock is so tiny that one astronaut is in the airlock headfirst and the other is in feet first.

GETTING SQUARE ASTRONAUTS OUT OF A ROUND AIRLOCK

Scientists have found that round containers are best for holding air pressure. But astronauts are in big bulky space suits with big square backpacks. To get out of a round airlock as a square-shaped astronaut with tethers and tools is no easy task. To do it gracefully and efficiently takes hours of practice.

WHAT THEY LEARN IN THE NBL

Underwater in their spacesuits, astronauts learn how to operate the suit, maneuver with the suit on, work with the tools they'll be using in space, think in three dimensions, communicate effectively with each other and spacewalk safely. Each astronaut must develop techniques to most efficiently make repairs or install equipment out in space. This practice is done in the NBL before ever stepping out into space.

Astronauts Soichi Noguichi of JAXA and NASA astronauts Stephen K. Robinson and Andrew SW Thomas training for spacewalks in the NBL in March 2005. Photo courtesy of NASA.

The Real Deal: Spacewalking in Space
SUITING UP AND PRE-BREATHING

For astronauts working on the American side of the ISS, suiting up and pre-breathing before heading out the airlock takes five hours.[16]

WHAT ASTRONAUTS DO WHILE SPACEWALKING

Astronauts perform spacewalks for a variety of reasons. They often need to perform maintenance or fix different things on the space station itself, other spacecraft or satellites. Sometimes they test out new equipment or perform experiments that can only be done in the vacuum of space.[17] Spacewalking is dangerous, so as many things as possible are done robotically. But some things simply have to be done in person.

TELL ME WHAT TO DO

Rather than memorizing everything they have to do in great detail or carrying around a handbook of instructions, astronauts will receive step-by-step instructions from ground control in Moscow or Houston, or from another astronaut inside the space station.

TOOLS DESIGNED FOR OUTER SPACE

Common tools like screwdrivers, wrenches, torque multipliers and drills are all used in space. However, these tools have to be carefully designed to work well in space with an astronaut who is wearing a pressurized suit and bulky gloves.[18]

WIRE TIES

Wire ties are flexible pieces of brass or copper wire with loops on both ends. An astronaut will use wire ties to quickly create a handhold or tether to something. Astronauts will also tie them around their gear, which makes it easy to attach tools to things. Russians invented the wire ties. The story goes that cosmonauts training at the Johnson Space Center in Houston saw the small wire twist ties on bread bags. They thought that was a simple and clever idea and created larger versions to tie things down in space.[19]

DOUBLE ATTACHMENTS

As a safety measure, spacewalkers must be attached to the spacecraft in two different ways. The first is the safety tether that is attached to the suit on a cable reel. It can be let out and reeled in as they move around the outside of the ISS.

Other ways that astronauts attach themselves to the space station are by gripping a handrail, locking their feet into a Portable Foot Restraint (PFR) found on different areas of the station or using the Body Restraint Tether (BRT). The BRT can stabilize the astronaut better than just the safety tether. It looks like a thick snake, but it's a heavy tool attached to the spacesuit on one end, and with a metal clamp on the other tend. When not in use, the BRT is folded up at the astronaut's side.[20]

SPACEWALKS AREN'T ACTUALLY WALKS

The official name for these space events is Extravehicular Activity, or EVA, but it became known as a spacewalk. However, this nickname isn't accurate, because astronauts don't actually walk in space! One astronaut described it as akin to swimming.[21] What astronauts actually do is move themselves along by pulling their bodies with a hand-over-hand motion along a path of rails that are attached to the space station. This hand-grasping motion is called "translating."[22]

TRANSLATION PATHS

The planned route for every spacewalk is called the translation path. Every translation path has been studied, practiced and modified for many hours—by the astronauts themselves and by a translation path development team—before it's ever performed in space. If the astronauts are assigned a new path that they weren't able to practice before their arrival, or if they want to study up on the path before the actual event, there is virtual reality software they can use on the ISS.[23]

IN CASE OF AN EMERGENCY, USE JETPACK

As part of the EMU spacesuit, there is an integrated emergency jet pack called SAFER (Simplified Aid for EVA Rescue). This jetpack has 24 small compressed nitrogen thrusters at hip and shoulder level. The jetpack makes it possible for an astronaut who becomes untethered and starts to drift away from the space station to use the thrusters and return to the station.[24]

Spacewalk Essentials

ADULT DIAPERS ARE A MUST

Astronauts wear adult diapers, or MAGs (Maximum Absorbent Garments) on launch and re-entry, but they also wear them while out on spacewalks that can last from 10-14 hours. It's critical for astronauts to stay hydrated...but this also means they will eventually need to relieve themselves. There is no easy alternative, so wearing an adult diaper is a must.

ASTRONAUTS PREPARE FOR EVERYTHING...EVERYTHING

One of the hardest things astronauts have to get used to is going to the bathroom in a diaper while lying down or standing up. To "train" for those situations, NASA sends a few of these diapers home with astronauts so they can practice using them. To prep for using them during launch and landing, astronauts are told to use them while lying down in their bathtubs.[25]

NUMBER TWO

As hard as it is for astronauts to pee in a diaper, going number two in a diaper just seems unthinkable. Astronauts will take medication in order to "clear the pipes" before a spacewalk so that it's not something they have to think about. No astronaut has had to find out what it's like to poo while on a spacewalk—at least not that has been shared publicly![26] I can imagine things like that would be one of those "What happens in space, stays in space" type of secrets.

LIQUID-COOLING GARMENTS

Spacewalking is hard work, and it's easy to become overheated. One astronaut found this out the hard way and it almost ended in disaster. Astronauts now wear a liquid cooling garment over their adult diaper. This long underwear-type garment acts like a built-in air conditioner once connected to the suit.[27]

SNOOPY CAP

Underneath their helmet, astronauts wear a cloth hat with earphones and a microphone in it. It's been nicknamed a "Snoopy cap" after the black and white cap the Peanuts character Snoopy wore when fighting the Red Baron. It has black over the ears and white stripe down the center. Apollo astronauts first called it the Snoopy cap and it's been called that ever since.

(*March 31, 2020*) NASA *astronaut Andrew Morgan wearing a communication cap, also known as the "Snoopy cap."* Photo courtesy of NASA.

 DID YOU KNOW

NASA has a long history with the *Peanuts* character Snoopy. The Apollo 10 lunar module was named Snoopy and the command module was named Charlie Brown. Snoopy has been to space as a plush toy a few different times and even to the International Space Station in celebration of the 20th anniversary of continuous human presence on the station. NASA honors its best employees and with the Silver Snoopy Award that has flown in space.

Most recently, a five-ounce, 10-inch-by-7-inch version of Snoopy will launch onboard a rocket bound for the Moon as part of the Artemis 1 unmanned mission. The plan is that Snoopy will circle the Moon and return to earth. This historic flight is planned for mid to late 2022.

This one-of-a kind Snoopy will be wearing a NASA space suit that's using only NASA-approved materials. This spacesuit meets all the same requirements and is the same quality that future Artemis astronauts will be wearing.[28]

FEELING HUNGRY?

To make it possible for astronauts to have something to eat during long days performing spacewalks, NASA added a holder inside the helmet to hold snacks like dried fruit rolls. It was positioned in a way so that the astronaut could bend their head down and take a bite. However, this didn't always go as planned. The fruit bar was next to the drink tube, which sometimes leaked a bit. This would turn the fruit bar into a "gooey mass" and made eating it a messy ordeal. They've since stopped using them.

THIRSTY?

To stay hydrated during a long day of spacewalking, astronauts attach a drink bag inside their suit. The drinking straw is positioned so that it's easy to take sips. It's the same type of straw used by long-distance cyclists with a bite valve that opens up when you squeeze the straw between your lips. It then closes when you're done. The bag can hold about a liter of water.[29]

INTENSELY HOT AND COLD

The sun rises and sets every 45 minutes while on the ISS. When you're not inside the comfortable 71°F (22°C) climate-controlled space station,[30] things can quickly get either toasty or chilly.

The temperatures vary, but they can dip as cold as -250°F (-156°C) or rise as hot as 250°F (121°C) in the sun.[31]

While the suit and the cooling garment have ways of protecting the astronaut against those extreme temperatures, they can still feel hot and cold. Their gloves now have warmers inside to help keep their hands warm—especially fingers. Astronauts try not to bump their legs against the suit when it's facing the sun because the suit itself gets hot.

Spacewalks Are Dangerous

HARD AND EXHAUSTING

It's difficult to move while wearing a spacesuit. It resists every motion that you make, pushing against every bend of the elbow or knees, twist of your waist and closing of your fist. It's like a workout for the entire 6-8 hours someone is working outside the ISS. Astronauts will often practice with hand grippers to strengthen their hands.

OVERHEATING

During the Gemini 9A mission in 1968, astronaut Gene Cernan performed a difficult two-hour spacewalk. EVAs were still very new at the time, and there weren't any handholds or footholds to help stabilize spacewalkers. Moving without anything to stabilize himself, Cernan worked extra hard and he began to sweat. His visor fogged up and he lost several pounds of weight due to sweating so much. After this almost disastrous EVA, astronauts began wearing cooling garments with integrated tubes that circulates cool water, which helps regulate body temperature.[32]

SUIT PUNCTURES

If a spacesuit were to get punctured during a spacewalk, it could present a serious problem—or even death. One problem that could happen is that all of the oxygen the astronaut needs to breathe escapes, and they would run out of air. Loss of pressure would cause the air in the astronaut's lungs to expand and damage the gas exchange processes inside. Water in the body would instantly vaporize, causing the astronaut's body to swell up and gases in the blood would form bubbles and stop blood from circulating. After passing out, the astronaut would die within two minutes from lack of oxygen.[33]

DROWNING TO DEATH

This almost happened to Italian astronaut Luca Parmitano during his spacewalk in July 2013. A clogged filter caused water to build up inside his helmet. Miraculously, he was able to get back inside the airlock in time for him to remove his deadly, water-filled helmet.[34]

FLOATING OFF INTO SPACE

Being thrown off the space station and floating helplessly into space is the stuff of nightmares. As of June 2022, no one has been lost in space this way. There are multiple safety precautions in place to prevent this from happening, such as safety tethers, the practice of spacewalking in pairs, external footholds and handholds and an integrated emergency jetpack as part of the spacesuit. Astronauts train for scenarios like this so that they can be avoided at all costs.

However, there has been one reported close call. On his first spacewalk, Russian cosmonaut Oleg Skripochka was working on the Russian service module on the ISS when he became untethered and started to drift away. The only thing that saved him from being the first person lost in space was that he hit an antenna. This impact was enough to send him floating back to the station close enough for him to grab onto a handrail.[35]

SPACE VERTIGO

Astronauts have been known to experience paralyzing fear when they realize that they're falling through space at a speed of 17,500 mph (27,600 kph). This is called EVA height vertigo. It's not a phobia, but a normal response to the new and terrifying reality of being in space.

Mir astronaut Jerry Linenger wrote in his memoir about the "dreadful and persistent" feeling that he was "plummeting earthward... at ten times or a hundred times faster" than what he'd experienced while free-falling as a skydiver.

A suit engineering corporation that worked with NASA shared the story of an unnamed astronaut who turned back around when exiting the hatch for an EVA, and was so scared he wrapped both of his space-suited arms around his co-astronaut's legs.[36]

BREAKAWAY EFFECT

There is a strange feeling of detachment from the Earth and a reality that has been described by those who have flown high altitudes—especially in orbit. For the majority of astronauts and pilots, this is a feeling of euphoria, not panic. But some have also freaked out. This is called the "Breakaway Effect." [37]

THE OVERVIEW EFFECT

While in space, some astronauts have also experienced what's called "The Overview Effect." It is the experience of seeing Earth from space, which delivers a kind of spiritual epiphany that changes a person's perspective on humanity forever. It's a feeling of wonder, privilege, reverence, clarity and awe that changes how you think and look at the world and humanity. It provides a clear perspective on the shared collective experience we have as humans. [38]

Out-of-This-World View

SURFING THE AURORA

Astronaut Chris Hadfield was the first Canadian to spacewalk, and the event is even marked on the back of the Canadian five-dollar bill. During his spacewalk, Commander Hadfield experienced the southern lights flowing through and around his legs. He's likened this experience to surfing the aurora. [39] The southern lights are also known as the aurora australis.

VERY DIFFERENT SUNRISES

We've only ever seen the sun against blue skies, but for the lucky few who get to go to space, they see something totally different: The sun against a very dark black backdrop. Not only that, but the sun rises and sets 16 times a day while on the ISS. This also means that the sun rises in the middle of the "night" while astronauts are sleeping!

DIFFERENT VIEW OF SHOOTING STARS

Hopefully all of us have seen a shooting star while looking up at the

Sunrise captured by astronaut Reid Wiseman onboard the ISS June 8, 2014. Photo taken by Reid Wiseman. Photo courtesy of NASA.

night sky. In space, the view of shooting stars is a little different. Astronauts see shooting stars *below* them because they are created as space rocks called meteors pass through Earth's atmosphere, which is underneath them!

STARS DON'T TWINKLE

On Earth, stars twinkle. In space, they don't. It all has to do with atmosphere. Because on the ground, we are looking at stars through the gases and water vapor that make up Earth's atmosphere, stars appear to twinkle. In space, the stars appear brighter and, and they don't twinkle because there is nothing blocking the path between their light and your eyeballs.[40]

PLANETS APPEAR BRIGHTER

Like stars, planets also appear brighter while in space and outside of Earth's atmosphere. There are a few planets that appear brighter than others: Jupiter, Mars, and Venus.[41]

Describing Earth from Space

"The color and brilliance of the planet, sprawling out in every direction, are startling. I've seen the Earth from spacecraft windows countless times now, but the difference between seeing the planet from inside a spacecraft, through multiple layers of bulletproof glass, and seeing it from out here is like the difference between seeing a mountain from a car window and climbing the peak."
- Scott Kelly

"I thought at one point, if you could be up in heaven, this is how you would see the planet. And then I dwelled on that and said, no, it's more beautiful than that. This is what heaven must look like. I think of our planet as a paradise. We are very lucky to be here."
- Mike Massimino [42]

"The overriding impression I got of life on Earth is how robust it is. Life has managed to essentially completely cover this planet in all sorts of different places—it finds a way."
- Ed Lu[43]

"Speaking of the Earth, it's hard to take your eyes off it. I can't get over seeing the curvature, and the thin layer of atmosphere that keeps us alive."
- Michael Anderson[44]

★ ★ ★

"From above our magnificent planet Earth the perspective is truly awe-inspiring...it is glorious. Even the stars have a special brightness."
- Laurel Clark[45]

★ ★ ★

"I have seen some incredible sights: lightning spreading over the Pacific, the aurora australis lighting up the entire visible horizon with the cityglow of Australia below, the crescent Moon setting over the limb of the Earth, the vast plains of Africa and the dunes on Cape Horn, rivers breaking through tall mountain passes, the scars of humanity, the continuous line of life extending from North America, through Central America and into South America, a crescent Moon setting over the limb [horizon] of our blue planet."
– Laurel Clark, in an excerpt from her final email home before Columbia disintegrated during re-entry.[46]

"There's no greater beauty than looking at the Earth from up high—and I'll never forget the first time I saw it. After take-off we left the atmosphere and suddenly light streamed in through the window. We were over the Pacific Ocean. The gloriously deep blue seas took my breath away."
– Helen Sharman[47]

NOTES

1. Mark Brown, "First Picture Drawn in Space to Appear in Cosmonauts Show in London," The Guardian (Guardian News and Media, August 31, 2015), https://www.theguardian.com/science/2015/aug/31/first-picture-space-cosmonauts-science-museum-alexei-leonov.

2. "Planetary Names: Crater, Craters: Leonov on Moon," Gazetteer of Planetary Nomenclature, last modified December 2, 2019, https://planetarynames.wr.usgs.gov/Feature/3352.

3. Bob Granath, "Gemini IV: Learning to Walk in Space," NASA (NASA, December 28, 2017), https://www.nasa.gov/feature/gemini-iv-learning-to-walk-in-space.

4. Wikipedia, s.v. "List of Spacewalkers," last modified May 2, 2021, https://en.wikipedia.org/wiki/List_of_spacewalkers.

5. Kevin Wilcox, "This Month in NASA History: Astronauts Make First Untethered Spacewalk," NASA (NASA, February 6, 2020), https://appel.nasa.gov/2020/02/06/this-month-in-nasa-history-astronauts-make-first-untethered-spacewalk/.

6. Gregory Cecil, "Our SpaceFlight Heritage: Bruce McCandless Performs the First Untethered EVA," SpaceFlight Insider, February 7, 2015, https://web.archive.org/web/20201108092921/

https://www.spaceflightinsider.com/space-flight-history/our-spaceflight-heritage-bruce-mccandless-performs-the-first-untethered-eva/.

7. Samantha Cristoforetti, *Diary of an Apprentice Astronaut*, trans. Jill Foulston (Penguin, 2020), 147, Kindle.

8. Wikipedia, "List of Space Walkers."

9. Chris Hadfield, "Spacewalking: Training," MasterClass (MasterClass), accessed May 31, 2021, https://www.masterclass.com/classes/chris-hadfield-teaches-space-exploration/chapters/spacewalking-training.

10. NASA, "The NBL Pool," Exploring Space Through Math, accessed May 30, 2021, https://www.nasa.gov/pdf/740536main_Geom-ST_Nspire_NBL.pdf.

11. Brian Dunbar, "About the Hubble Space Telescope," ed. Rob Garner, NASA (NASA, last modified December 18, 2018), https://www.nasa.gov/mission_pages/hubble/story/index.html.

12. Michael J. Neufeld and John B. Charles, "Practicing for Space Underwater: Inventing Neutral Buoyancy Training, 1963–1968," *Endeavour* 39, no. 3-4 (2015): pp. 147-159, https://airandspace.si.edu/files/pdf/research/neufeld-charles-neutral-buoyancy.pdf.

13. Hadfield, "Spacewalking."

14. Hadfield, "Spacewalking."

15. "Sonny Carter Training Facility: The Neutral Buoyancy Laboratory," NASA, 2006, https://www.nasa.gov/centers/johnson/pdf/167748main_FS_NBL508c.pdf.

16. Samantha Cristoforetti, *Diary of an Apprentice Astronaut*, trans. Jill Foulston (Penguin, 2020), 319, Kindle.

17. Brian Dunbar, "What Is a Spacewalk?," ed. Flint Wild, NASA (NASA, July 27, 2020), https://www.nasa.gov/audience/forstudents/k-4/stories/nasa-knows/what-is-a-spacewalk-k4.html.

18. Cristoforetti, *Diary of an Apprentice Astronaut*, 62.

19. Mary Robinette Kowal (@MaryRobinette), "Wire Ties! These Are Brass Wires That They Use to Tie Things down. The Story Goes That Cosmonauts Were Training at JSC and Saw the Wire Ties on Bread. They Thought That Was Neat and Created Larger Versions to Tie Things down in Space. NASA Saw THOSE and Created Their Own. Pic. twitter.com/Tk3Knt0WSL," Twitter, April 8, 2019, https://twitter.com/MaryRobinette/status/1115265803115532288.

20. Cristoforetti, *Diary of an Apprentice Astronaut*, 63.

21. "Working | Outside the Spacecraft," Smithsonian Air and Space Museum, accessed May 31, 2021, https://airandspace.si.edu/exhibitions/outside-the-spacecraft/online/orbit.cfm.

22. Scott Kelly, *Endurance: A Year in Space, A Lifetime of Discovery* (New York: Alfred A. Knopf, 2017), 280.

23. Terry Virts, *How to Astronaut: An Insider's Guide to Leaving Planet Earth* (New York, Workman Publishing, 2020), 154.

24. Cristoforetti, *Diary of an Apprentice Astronaut*, 64.

25. Virts, *How to Astronaut*, 67-68.

26. Virts, *How to Astronaut*, 70.

27. Kelly, *Endurance*, 279.

28. Ayumi Davis, "One Small Step for Man, One Giant Leap for Snoopy: Plush Version Scheduled for Rocket Ride," Newsweek.com, November 12, 2021, https://www.newsweek.com/one-small-step-man-one-giant-leap-snoopy-plush-version-scheduled-rocket-ride-1648817.

29. Cristoforetti, *Diary of an Apprentice Astronaut*, 92.

30. Ally, "20 Questions for 20 Years: Happy Birthday International Space Station," ESA (European Space Agency, November 21, 2018), https://blogs.esa.int/alexander-gerst/2018/11/21/spacestationfaqs/.

31. Brian Dunbar, "Spacesuit Basics," ed. Erin Mahoney, NASA (NASA, July 17, 2020), https://www.nasa.gov/feature/spacewalk-spacesuit-basics.

32. "Floating | Outside the Spacecraft," Smithsonian Air and Space Museum, accessed May 31, 2021, https://airandspace.si.edu/exhibitions/outside-the-spacecraft/online/floating.cfm.

33. Anna Gosline, "Survival in Space Unprotected Is Possible--Briefly," Scientific American (Scientific American, February 14, 2008), https://www.scientificamerican.com/article/survival-in-space-unprotected-possible/.

34. Kelly, Endurance, 278.

35. Kelly, Endurance, 276.

36. Mary Roach, Packing for Mars: The Curious Science of Life in the Void (New York, NY: WW Norton, 2011), 71.

37. Sydney Brownstone, "The Break-Off Effect," Fast Company (Fast Company, May 2, 2017), https://www.fastcompany.com/3036887/out-of-this-world-the-mysterious-mental-side-effects-of-traveling-into-space-2.

38. Chris Hadfield: How Looking at 4 Billion Years of Earth's History Changes You | Big Think, YouTube (Big Think, 2018), https://www.youtube.com/watch?v=qPvSRPsWhOQ.

39. Chris Hadfield, "Spacewalking: Spacewalks," MasterClass (MasterClass, May 27, 2021), https://www.masterclass.com/classes/chris-hadfield-teaches-space-exploration/chapters/spacewalking-spacewalks.

40. "Why Do Stars Twinkle?," Scientific American (Scientific American, October 24, 2005), https://www.scientificamerican.com/article/why-do-stars-twinkle/.

41. Ally, "20 Questions for 20 Years."

42. Nadia Drake, "These Astronauts Saw Earth From Space. Here's How It Changed Them.," National Geographic, March 2018, https://www.nationalgeographic.com/magazine/2018/03/astronauts-space-earth-perspective.

43. Drake, "Earth From Space."

44. Jonathan Martin and David Postman, "Michael Anderson: From Humble Roots to One of America's 'Humble Heroes'," The Seattle Times (The Seattle Times Company, February 9, 2003), https://archive.seattletimes.com/archive/?date=20030209&slug=anderson09m.

45. Alexander Voss, "Racine Remembers a Hero: Laurel Clark Letter Home," Racine.wi.net, March 13, 2007, https://web.archive.org/web/20070313102022/http://racine.wi.net/clarkletter.html.

46. Voss, "Racine Remembers a Hero."

47. Michael Segalov, "Helen Sharman: 'There's No Greater Beauty than Seeing the Earth from up High'," The Guardian (Guardian News and Media, January 5, 2020), https://www.theguardian.com/lifeandstyle/2020/jan/05/astronaut-helen-sharman-this-much-i-know.

SPACE FOOD: WHAT ASTRONAUTS CAN & CAN'T EAT

Space Food Firsts

FIRST PERSON TO EAT IN SPACE

The first human in space was also the first person to eat in space. During his 108-minute flight, Yuri Gagarin ate beef and liver paste squeezed from a toothpaste-like tube for dinner followed by a tube of chocolate sauce for dessert.[1]

FIRST FOOD IN SPACE

While Gagarin was the first human to consume food in space, this doesn't mean this was the first food in space. Before Gagarin's tube meal, Russian space dog Laika dined on a meal of powdered meat and breadcrumb gelatin during her trip to space.[2]

FIRST AMERICAN TO EAT IN SPACE

A year after Gagarin had his first meal in space, John Glenn became the first American to eat in space. Glenn's first meal onboard Friendship 7 during his 4 hour and 55-minute mission was applesauce eaten from a tube and sugar cubes that he mixed with water. Alan Shepard was the first American in space, but because his flight lasted only 15 minutes, there wasn't time to eat.

WHY TOOTHPASTE TUBES?

In the early days of space travel, scientists didn't yet know how swallowing and digesting food in microgravity would work. So, food was pureed and put into aluminum toothpaste-like tubes that could be easily squeezed into the astronaut's mouth.

Early in the space program, this is what space food looked like: beef and vegetables in an aluminum tube. This is an example of what astronauts ate during the Mercury space programs. Photo courtesy of NASA.

FIRST FOOD EATEN ON THE MOON

While it wasn't broadcast to the world, the first food eaten on the Moon was actually the communion wafer and wine that Buzz Aldrin brought with him. Aldrin's communion experience happened shortly after they landed at the Sea of Tranquility, but before their scheduled meal.[3]

The scheduled meal that Armstrong and Aldrin ate on the Moon included bacon. It turns out that bacon travels well—especially if it's packed in cubes. Shortly after landing at the Sea of Tranquility, Armstrong and Aldrin ate the first meal on the Moon. Their meal included bacon squares, peaches, sugar cookie cubes, rehydrated pineapple grapefruit drink and coffee.[4]

Armstrong and Aldrin had four separate meals while on the Moon. Any leftovers and trash are still there on the lunar module.[5]

FIRST BISCUITS ON THE MOON

It's rumored that the first biscuit on the Moon was a British Bourbon biscuit eaten by Buzz Aldrin. To Americans, biscuits would be a cookie.

Bourbons are a chocolate sandwich cookie about the size of a domino and filled with a smooth chocolate buttercream filling.[6]

FIRST COOKED MEAL IN SPACE

Pretty much all food in space comes up precooked or in its natural state. In 2008, NASA astronaut Sandra Magnus became the first person to cook a meal in space. She used the space station's food warmer to cook onions and garlic, which took over an hour. However, she was able to create an impressive and delicious meal: mesquite grilled tuna in a lemon-garlic-ginger marinade. It was eaten from a bag, but the meal was made in space.[7]

FIRST BAKED FOODS IN SPACE

Just in time for Santa in December 2019, the crew onboard the ISS baked chocolate chip cookies in space. They used premade cookie dough that had been provided by DoubleTree by Hilton and used an

(May 2015) ESA astronaut Samantha Cristoforetti enjoys the first espresso in space made with the new ISSpresso machine. Photo by Scott Kelly. Photo courtesy of NASA.

experimental space oven. It took two hours, but by the end they had cookies and milk ready for Santa.[8]

FIRST ESPRESSO IN SPACE

In May 2015, Italian astronaut Samantha Cristoforetti became the first person to drink freshly brewed coffee in space using a special espresso machine called the ISSpresso. Besides coffee, it can brew tea, hot chocolate and broth.[9]

THE $1,000,000 PIZZA DELIVERY

Pizza Hut paid the Russian space agency to deliver a specially made pizza in a resupply vehicle to the International Space Station in 2001. This special delivery made history and made the Russian cosmonaut onboard very happy. While traditional Pizza Hut pizza comes with pepperoni, they had to settle with salami. Apparently, pepperoni doesn't pass the strict space food test![10]

PIZZA ORDERED FROM SPACE SHUTTLE

Astronaut Mike Massimino's pizza craving was so bad that he ordered a pizza from space. He arranged to have it delivered to their hotel near the Kennedy Space Center where they'd be staying once they returned to Earth.[11]

EAT WHAT YOU GROW

If humans are going to make it to Mars, we are going to have to grow our food in space. Astronauts have been experimenting with growing a variety of different plants in space. Recently, astronauts on the ISS successfully grew a crop of lettuce and tested it out by eating it. It seemed to taste just like Earth lettuce, if that's your thing.

Variety & Thinking Ahead

In the early days of NASA's space program, there wasn't much variety when it came to the food astronauts ate in space. But having good food—and a variety to choose from—makes a huge difference in the

Cosmonaut Anton Shkaplerov eats lettuce grown and harvested in orbit on the ISS. Photo by Scott Tingle. Photo courtesy of NASA.

mood and morale of the astronauts. There are now companies and entire departments at NASA devoted to space food. Their job is to provide foods that are healthy, safe for space and, most importantly, taste good.

Since storage is limited on the spacecraft astronauts ride to the ISS, food deliveries come up in separate cargo resupply launches. This means astronauts have to choose their meals about five months in advance so they can be packed, launched and waiting for them at the ISS when they arrive.

TASTE TESTING

As of 2022, astronauts can choose from more than 100 standard space food and drink offerings both from NASA and Russia. Months before heading into space, astronauts sample different food and drink options, see what former astronauts have had and see what's available from the standard menu. They use this information to plan their personal preference menu.[12] It's then reviewed by a dietitian who makes recommendations to ensure that each astronaut is getting the nutrients they need.

What's on the Menu?

THE DIFFERENT TYPES OF FOOD IN SPACE

The food eaten on the ISS is either rehydratable, thermostabilized, irradiated, partially dried, fresh, off-the-shelf food or extended life foods. Space food needs to be lightweight, compact and calorie-dense.

FRESH FOOD

When cargo resupply ships arrive at the ISS, a small supply of fresh fruits and vegetables are included. Things like apples, oranges and carrots are all welcome treats. These are eaten quickly by the crew since things tend to spoil quicker in space, but also because it was something different than the packaged foods they have been eating for months.[13]

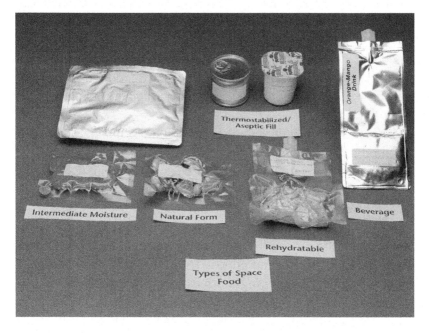

A few examples of space food. At the top left, Beef tips w/mushroom pouch, top center shows peach yogurt and butterscotch pudding. Top right is an orange-mango drink mix. Bottom from left to right: Dried apricots, trail mix, and shrimp cocktail. Photo courtesy of NASA.

REHYDRATABLE

These meals are similar to what you might take backpacking. They are lightweight, come in clear packages and all you need to do is add hot water. Almost any food can be dehydrated or freeze-dried. Examples of rehydratable foods eaten on the space station are mac and cheese, mashed potatoes, different types of soup, chicken and rice, shrimp cocktail and scrambled eggs.[14]

THERMOSTABALIZED

Thermostabilized food has been heat-treated to kill bacteria. Food that comes in cans, plastic cups and sealed flexible plastic pouches has typically been thermostabilized. This includes canned fish like tuna and salmon, canned fruit and pudding. Food in the pouches can be reheated in the pouch and is often eaten straight from the package. Many main dishes come in thermostabilized pouches, like beef tips with mushrooms, tomatoes and eggplant, ham and chicken ala king.[15] The food can be warmed up in a warming oven that's about the size of a suitcase.

IRRADIATED

Food that has been irradiated has been sterilized with ionizing radiation that keeps the food from going bad. Meat is the only food that is irradiated for the ISS. For example, beef steak is cooked, packaged into foil-laminated pouches, exposed briefly to radiation and then it's ready to go. This kills any bacteria and makes the meat shelf stable. Beef steak and smoked turkey are the only two irradiated food items available on the International Space Station.[16]

PARTIALLY DRIED

Food that has had most of the moisture removed to increase the time it takes to spoil includes things like sausages, jerky, partially-dried fruit like raisins, apricots, mango, apples and pineapple.

OFF-THE-SHELF FOOD

Items that you'd find at your local grocery store like cookies, chocolate, candies, olives, tuna packets and nuts are space safe and can also be found onboard the ISS.[17] Space safe means it's been reviewed and approved by the agency sending the astronauts into space.

EXTENDED LIFE FOODS

A lot of the off-the-shelf foods available on the ISS also fall under the extended life foods. Items like beef jerky, dried fruit, nuts, cookies, and chocolate.

SPACE BEVERAGES

Any drink that can be made into a powder form and then rehydrated is available on the ISS as a space drink. Astronauts can drink fruit juice, Tang, lemonade, apple cider, tea, coffee, hot cocoa, milk, smoothies and breakfast drinks.[18]

IT'S ALL ABOUT THE SAUCE

A common question you'll hear during mealtimes onboard the ISS is "What are you having with your sauce today?" Condiments are king when it comes to eating well on the ISS. Things don't taste quite the same in space as they do on Earth. It may have something to do with the fluid shift that happens in astronauts' bodies that causes them to be more congested. Adding condiments that add flavor and spice to whatever they're eating definitely adds to the taste. Hot sauce, horseradish, mayonnaise, BBQ sauce, dried tomato paste, pesto paste, olive oil and ketchup are all very popular among the crew.[19]

SMALL PORTION SIZES

In an effort to prevent waste, the space food portions are small. This also means that astronauts can eat several different things at one meal.[20]

SAMPLE MENU

Astronauts eat three meals per day with snacks. Here's an example of a week-long menu for an astronaut.

BREAKFAST	LUNCH	DINNER	SNACKS/ DESSERT	BEVERAGES
Scrambled eggs	Split-pea soup	BBQ beef brisket	Chocolate pudding cake	Coffee
Oatmeal	Chicken in salsa	Beef ravioli	Apricot cobbler	Tea
Granola	Pasta with shrimp (prawns)	Chicken with peanut sauce	Granola bar	Powdered milk
Sausage patties	Tuna-salad spread	Potato medley	Macadamia nuts	Cocoa
Dried Fruit	Broccoli au gratin	Red beans and rice	Lemon-curd cake	Orange/ Lemon/Lime
Maple-top muffin	Tomatoes & Eggplant	Creamed spinach	Butter cookies	Strawberry breakfast drink

Tim Peake's ISS menu example from "Ask an Astronaut" [21]

Special Space Foods

BACON SQUARE

To make bacon space-safe, it is squeezed under a hydraulic press to make it compact and crumble-free. The result is square-shaped, which is how it got its name.[22]

TANG: THE SPACE DRINK NASA DIDN'T INVENT

Many people think that NASA invented Tang, but they did not. However, NASA does buy the fruit drink mix in bulk, and sends it to space labeled as "orange drink." General Foods Corporation actually invented the drink in 1957. It wasn't very popular until NASA sent it to space with John Glenn on Friendship 7. It's unclear whether Glenn drank it during his flight, but that didn't matter. Tang made it to space, and has been to space ever since—even to the Moon!

Tang in space looks different than it does on the ground. In space, Tang comes in a sealed pouch which astronauts add water to using a water dispenser and a special adapter on the pouch. Then they shake it up and drink it using a special locking straw. [23]

GRITS IN SPACE

Grits are a Southern American delicacy, and North Carolina-native Charlie Duke asked for grits when he flew into space. It took NASA two or three tries to get it just right, but according to Duke, they succeeded and he ate all of his.[24]

FAMOUS SUGAR COOKIES

Rita Rapp was a food scientist and the head of the Apollo Food System team. Her goal was to turn space food from "cubes and tubes" into something astronauts could eat in a normal, Earth-like way and something that they would get excited about eating.

Her sugar cookies were a famous motivational tool among astronauts and were even treated as currency. According to astronaut Owen Garriott, who was onboard Skylab for 59 days, he and his crew members would bribe other crew mates to do something for them with sugar cookies from their personal stash.[25]

PARTIALLY-DEHYDRATED TORTILLAS

Bread is not allowed on the American side of the ISS. Russians have bread cubes, but everyone else substitutes with tortillas. NASA used to buy fresh tortillas the day before launch to send with the space shuttle astronauts. The tortillas onboard the ISS are partially-dehydrated, and made by the same company that Taco Bell uses for their tortillas. Tortillas work well in space because they don't crumble, but also because they have a long shelf life.[26]

MOST POPULAR MEAL: FREEZE-DRIED SHRIMP COCKTAIL

NASA has been sending shrimp cocktail up with astronauts since the Gemini days, and astronauts have been huge fans. The shrimp cocktail with red horseradish sauce has been one of the most-requested

Commander Peggy A. Whitson using a tortilla instead of the traditional hamburger bun to make a hamburger onboard the ISS. Photo courtesy of NASA.

foods since space food was invented. It may have something to do with the fact that astronauts' taste becomes dulled, but it is a crew favorite. Astronaut Story Musgrave used to eat shrimp cocktail at every meal—even breakfast! [27]

CHOCOLATE AND SPACE JUST GO TOGETHER

When the first man went to space, he had chocolate sauce for dessert. Whether it's chocolate pudding, hot chocolate, chocolate candies or chocolate bars, chocolate in some form has been in space for as long as man has. Since NASA doesn't endorse any brands, the chocolate onboard is often labeled with generic names. But according to the space history and artifacts website, collectSPACE.com, many name brands have had their time in space. Astronauts have enjoyed Dove Bars, Ghirardelli, Kit Kats, Snickers, Raisinets, Reese's Peanut Butter Cups, Twix, M&Ms, Toblerone and, of course, Milky Way Bars.

ASTRONAUTS' CANDY OF CHOICE: M&Ms®

While they're not technically called M&Ms® in space, candy-coated chocolates are the candy of choice onboard the International Space Station. They're the perfect snack. They don't crumble, you can eat several at a time, they do cool stuff in microgravity, can be used as science demonstrations and of course they "melt in your mouth, not in your hand." [28]

(August 8, 1992) Astronaut Loren J. Shriver chasing down floating M&Ms while orbiting Earth onboard Space Shuttle Atlantis. Photo courtesy of NASA.

THANKSGIVING DINNER IN SPACE

To make Thanksgiving as festive and as familiar as possible, astronauts have enjoyed smoked turkey, cornbread dressing, green bean casserole, candied yams, and fruit cobbler, washed down with some sort of rehydratable powdered drink (alcohol is not allowed onboard.) [29]

LEAST POPULAR FOOD

Maybe because they can lead to flatulence, or simply because astronauts just don't care for them, but Brussels sprouts are the least-requested food item for those headed to the ISS.

International Food Options

It's common for crews onboard the space station to share and trade food with others. Not only does it help add variety to the meals they can eat, but this practice also allows them to enjoy each other's culture.

RUSSIAN FOOD

The Russian crews onboard the ISS have a selection of over 300 food options to choose from. This includes fish, mashed potatoes, soup, borscht, cottage cheese with apple puree and even real bread. This bread comes in the form of dark rye sourdough mini loafs[30] that can be eaten in one bite. Here's an example of what cosmonauts eat on the International Space Station:

- **Breakfast:** curds and nuts, mashed potatoes with nuts, apple-quince chip sticks, sugarless coffee and vitamins
- **Lunch:** jellied pike perch, borscht with meat, goulash with buckwheat, bread, black currant juice and sugarless tea
- **Supper:** rice and meat, broccoli and cheese, nuts and tea with sugar
- **Second supper:** dried beef, cashew nuts, peaches and grape juice

The Russian Laboratory of Space Food has made many of their made-for-space food available to the public. People say eating borscht from a tube is not only handy while driving, but tastes just like the real thing.[31]

BRITISH, ITALIAN AND GERMAN FOOD

British astronaut Tim Peak had sausage mash, bacon sarnies (sandwiches), chicken curry, whisky-flavored fudge, Yorkshire tea and Scottish shortbread.[32]

Italian lasagna and German Käsespätzle have also made their way to the International Space Station.[33]

JAPANESE FOOD

The Japanese have been able to develop traditional Japanese foods that work well in space. Foods and drinks like matcha, ramen, sushi, soups, sashimi, yōkan (a dessert made from red bean paste), tofu, udon and rice with ume (Japanese pickled plums)[34] have all made their way to the International Space Station.[35]

KOREAN FOOD

South Korea's first astronaut, Yi So-yeon, brought a version of Korea's national dish: kimchi. This space-safe fermented cabbage dish took several years and over $1 million to develop.[36]

CHINESE FOOD

China isn't an International Space Station partner, but they have their own space program and have sent 11 taikonauts to space. Some of the food they've developed for space include Kung Pao chicken, yuxiang pork, Eight Treasure rice and Chinese herbal tea. This special space-safe food has been made available for sale to the public.

Thou Shalt Not Eat These Foods in Space

Space makes eating interesting, but there are some foods that don't work well in microgravity or can make being stuck in a confined space a toxic situation. Here are some foods that are not allowed in space.

REGULAR SALT AND PEPPER

Believe it or not, salt and pepper are not allowed on the ISS. Without gravity, the tiny particles would float away. Instead, astronauts use salt and pepper in a liquid form. Pepper is suspended in oil and salt is dissolved in water and both are kept in small bottles. If they weren't in liquid form, they would damage equipment, clog vents and could even get into the astronauts' eyes.[37]

CARBONATED DRINKS & BURPING IN SPACE

There are several reasons why carbonated drinks aren't allowed in space. One of the biggest ones is that astronauts cannot burp normally in space. When you eat in microgravity, the food and liquids you swallow float high in your stomach. When you burp, the air passes through a sphincter located at the top of your stomach. So, in space, your burps tend to be wet, not dry and more than air comes up.[38]

FISH

Fish tends to be very smelly. The space station is a confined space and you can't just open a window. So, you won't find much fish onboard. There are a few exceptions, but for the most part fish is left on Earth.[39]

CHIPS

There's nothing better than biting into a nice crunchy chip. But in space it's a no-no. Your chip crumbs could quickly float away and wreak havoc on space equipment. Like salt, chips can also clog vents and get in someone's eye. Chips are part of the crumbly food category and are not allowed.

ALCOHOL

Unless it's part of a science experiment, NASA does not allow alcohol onboard the International Space Station. However, communion wine did make it to the Moon before the ban. Buzz Aldrin drank communion wine during his own private communion service shortly after landing on the Moon.[40]

BREAD

If it crumbles, it doesn't go to space. Bread tends to be crumbly, so bread in its normal state doesn't fly. Instead, tortillas are used in its place. On the Russian side, they do have small bread cubes. But the bread you and I are familiar with isn't on the menu.[41]

THE CORNED BEEF SANDWICH INCIDENT

On Gemini 3, Astronaut John Young smuggled a corned beef sandwich into his pocket right before launch. He later revealed it after launch, surprising crew member Gus Grissom with it. Grissom took a bite, but it started to break apart and was quickly pocketed. The incident caused a review by the congressional Committee of Appropriations, and NASA had to promise to take steps "to prevent recurrence of corned-beef sandwiches in future flights."[42]

REINDEER JERKY

Reindeer meat is a common food in the Nordic countries, so it makes sense that Swedish astronaut Christer Fuglesang would want to bring some along with him. Maybe because the mission was so close to Christmas, some people thought it would be "weird" for the American astronauts. So Fuglesang brought moose jerky instead.[43]

ASTRONAUT ICE CREAM IS A LIE

If you think about it, freeze-dried astronaut ice cream is one of the crumbliest foods you could eat. If bread and chips aren't allowed, there's no way NASA would allow what is sold as astronaut ice cream in space. An astronaut did request ice cream during the Apollo program, but what actually flew was a synthetic cube that was dairy-based. It wasn't anything like what we know as astronaut ice cream and what you find in science museum gift shops.

The only ice cream astronauts eat on the International Space Station today is normal ice cream and it comes up in freezers in resupply vehicles. The freezers are for experiment samples, but instead of sending up empty freezers, NASA takes advantage of that empty space and sends the ISS crew frozen treats. This isn't a common occurrence, but it's a special treat when it does happen.[44]

Bonus Food, Mystery Food and Care Packages

To help provide variety and allow astronauts to bring a little bit of home with them, they are allowed to bring nine personal bonus containers of food about the size of a large shoe box.

BONUS FOOD

Astronauts get to choose food beyond the standard menu and can pick food from the NASA, Roscosmos, European or Japanese menus. Bonus food can also be NASA-approved off-the-shelf products. Some astronauts work with famous chefs to create the food they will include in their bonus food. All of it has to be approved by NASA and have certain shelf-life and safe-for-space requirements.

For example, Peggy Whitson brought rehydratable hamburger patties and special dinner rolls so she could make space hamburgers.[45] British astronaut Tim Peake figured out a way to have a specially-made "bacon sarnie" (bacon sandwich) as a bonus food.[46] Samantha Cristoforetti had off-the-shelf dark chocolate, tahini and pumpkin-seed bars. She also worked with a chef to bring bean soup, quinoa salad with mackerel and cherry tomatoes, and chicken curry with peas and mushrooms.[47]

MYSTERY FOOD

Who doesn't love a little bit of mystery? In 2008, the crew onboard the ISS received cans that were labeled "tasty snacks."[48] A fruitcake about the size of a trash can lid was found by a few astronauts who didn't know where it had come from, but they enjoyed the sweet treat for about a week.[49]

CARE PACKAGES

Resupply cargo ships often dock at the ISS. They contain experiments, water, oxygen and care packages for the crew. These care packages contain a variety of things like letters and photos from family and often treats in the form of food—things like beef jerky and chocolate candy.[50] Some have even received safe-for-space birthday cake.[51]

Birthday goodies! SpaceX Dragon sent up some special macaróns to celebrate astronaut Thomas Pesquet's birthday. Photo courtesy of NASA.

DID YOU KNOW?

One of the biggest manufacturers of space food is Bulgaria. They produce many of the foods used by space programs around the world. Things like rice pudding, yogurt, meatball soup and chicken and peas are all food items they make safe-for-space.[52]

NOTES

1. Eric Betz, "First Food in Space: Toothpaste Tubes of Applesauce and Beef," Discover Magazine, February 28, 2020, https://www.discovermagazine.com/the-sciences/first-food-in-space-toothpaste-tubes-of-applesauce-and-beef.

2. Mary Roach, Packing for Mars: The Curious Science of Life in the Void (New York, NY: WW Norton, 2011), 295.

3. David Mikkelson, "Did Buzz Aldrin Take Communion on the Moon?," Snopes.com, March 7, 2010, https://www.snopes.com/fact-check/communion-moon/.

4. Amy Shira Teitel, "When Bacon Flew to the Moon; or, #Spacebacon," Popular Science, April 7, 2014, https://www.popsci.com/blog-network/vintage-space/when-bacon-flew-moon-or-spacebacon/.

5. Claire Suddath, "What Do Astronauts Eat in Space?," Time (Time Inc., July 20, 2009), http://content.time.com/time/health/article/0,8599,1911617,00.html.

6. "Bourbon Biscuit: The First Biscuit on the Moon," Biscuit people, December 4, 2020, https://www.biscuitpeople.com/magazine/post/bourbon-biscuit.

7. Suddath, "What Do Astronauts Eat in Space?"

8. "Space Cookies: First Food Baked in Space by Astronauts," BBC News (BBC, January 24, 2020), https://www.bbc.com/news/world-51235555#.

9. "ISSpresso Gets Back from Space," Italian Food News, December 18, 2017, https://news.italianfood.net/2017/12/18/isspresso-gets-back-space/.

10. "Pizza Sets New Delivery Record," BBC News (BBC, May 22, 2001), http://news.bbc.co.uk/2/hi/americas/1345139.stm.

11. Former NASA Astronaut Explains How Food Is Different in Space: WIRED, YouTube (Wired, 2019), https://youtu.be/E36F4XG5zcY?t=171.

12. "Eating in Space," ESA (European Space Agency, last modified July 5, 2011), https://www.esa.int/kids/en/learn/Life_in_Space/Living_in_space/Eating_in_space.

13. Terry Virts, How to Astronaut: An Insider's Guide to Leaving Planet Earth (New York, Workman Publishing, 2020), 104.

14. Kim Dismukes, "Food for Space Flight," Human Space Flight (NASA, April 7, 2002), https://web.archive.org/web/20210123124821/https://spaceflight.nasa.gov/shuttle/reference/factsheets/food.html.

15. Dismukes, "Food for Space Flight."

16. "Space Food and Nutrition: Activity 4: Classifying Space Food," NASA 1999, https://www.nasa.gov/pdf/190537main_Classifying_Space_Food.pdf.

17. Virts, *How to Astronaut*, 292.

18. Virts, *How to Astronaut*, 104.

19. Peggy Whitson, "Peggy Whitson's Journal: It's All About the Sauce," ed. Amiko Kaudere, NASA (NASA, last modified October 23, 2010), https://www.nasa.gov/mission_pages/station/expeditions/expedition16/journal_peggy_whitson_5.html.

20. Scott Kelly, *Endurance: A Year in Space, A Lifetime of Discovery* (New York: Alfred A. Knopf, 2017), 79.

21. Tim Peake, *Ask an Astronaut: My Guide to Life in Space* (Little Brown and Company, 2017), 123.

22. Mary Roach, *Packing for Mars: The Curious Science of Life in the Void* (New York, NY: WW Norton, 2011), 288.

23. Matt Blitz, "How NASA Made Tang Cool," Food & Wine, March 18, 2017, https://www.foodandwine.com/lifestyle/how-nasa-made-tang-cool.

24. "The Woman Who Got Real Food to Space," National Air and Space Museum, April 9, 2018, https://airandspace.si.edu/stories/editorial/woman-who-got-real-food-space.

25. Thomas D. Jones, "Orbiting in a Fuel Tank," Air & Space Magazine, December 2013, https://www.airspacemag.com/space/orbiting-in-a-fuel-tank-180947752/.

26. Suddath, "What Do Astronauts Eat in Space?"

27. Megan Garber, "Astronauts' Favorite Space Food: Shrimp Cocktail," The Atlantic (Atlantic Media Company, April 9, 2013), https://www.theatlantic.com/technology/archive/2013/04/astronauts-favorite-space-food-shrimp-cocktail/274823/.

28. "Astronauts' Candy-Coated Space Snacks," National Air and Space Museum, October 31, 2017, https://airandspace.si.edu/stories/editorial/astronauts-candy-space-snacks.

29. Valerie Neal, "Thanksgiving Day in Space," National Air and Space Museum, November 27, 2014, https://airandspace.si.edu/stories/editorial/thanksgiving-day-space.

30. Virts, *How to Astronaut*, 105-106.

31. Anastasia Stepanova, "How Russian Space Food Has Evolved over the Years," Russia Beyond, June 24, 2018, https://www.rbth.com/russian-kitchen/328572-russian-space-food-evolution.

32. Peake, *Ask an Astronaut*, 122.

33. Samantha Cristoforetti, *Diary of an Apprentice Astronaut*, trans. Jill Foulston (Penguin, 2020), 157, Kindle.

34. Stefano Carnazzi, "What Astronauts Can and Can't Eat in Space," LifeGate, April 12, 2017, https://www.lifegate.com/austronauts-food-in-space.

35. "About Certification of 'Space Japanese Food,'" JAXA, June 27, 2007, https://www.jaxa.jp/press/2007/06/20070627_spacefood_j.html.

36. Choe Sang-hun, "Starship Kimchi: A Bold Taste Goes Where It Has Never Gone Before," The New York Times, February 24, 2008, https://www.nytimes.com/2008/02/24/world/asia/24kimchi.html.

37. Brian Dunbar, "Salt and Pepper Dispensers (2007)," NASA (NASA, July 7, 2014), https://www.nasa.gov/audience/forstudents/k-4/stories/salt-and-pepper-dispensers.html.

38. Marina Koren, "Everything You Never Thought to Ask About Astronaut Food," The Atlantic (Atlantic Media Company, December 15, 2017), https://www.theatlantic.com/science/archive/2017/12/astronaut-food-international-space-station/548255/.

39. Carnazzi, "What Astronauts Can and Can't Eat in Space."

40. Mikkelson, "Communion on the Moon?."

41. Beth Dreher, "7 Foods That Are Banned from Space," Reader's Digest, last modified April 29, 2021, https://www.rd.com/list/foods-banned-space/.

42. Elizabeth Howell, "How John Young Smuggled a Corned-Beef Sandwich into Space," Space. com, January 10, 2018, https://www.space.com/39341-john-young-smuggled-corned-beef-space.html.

43. "Christer Fuglesang Ready for Space after 14 Years of Training," Dagens Nyheter, November 16, 2007, https://web.archive.org/web/20071001090818/http:/www.dn.se/DNet/jsp/polopoly.jsp?d=2597&a=589321&previousRenderType=6.

44. Ker Than, "The Rich and Flavorful History of Chocolate in Space," Smithsonian.com (Smithsonian Institution, February 10, 2015), https://www.smithsonianmag.com/science-nature/rich-and-flavorful-history-chocolate-space-180954160/.

45. Whitson, "It's All About the Sauce."

46. Kelly, Endurance, 327.

47. Cristoforetti, Diary of an Apprentice Astronaut, 157.

48. Carnazzi, "What Astronauts Can and Can't Eat in Space."

49. Amanda Wills, "7 Oddball Things Found on the Space Station," Mashable (Mashable, July 7, 2013), https://mashable.com/2013/07/07/odd-things-space-station/.

50. Virts, How to Astronaut, 106.

51. Suddath, What Do Astronauts Eat in Space?."

52. U.S. Embassy Sofia, "'Space' Food?," U.S. Embassy in Bulgaria, March 11, 2018, https://bg.usembassy.gov/space-food.

GOING TO THE BATHROOM IN SPACE

Maybe because it's a universal function and we all gotta go, the question astronauts are asked most often about their time in space is "How do you go to the bathroom?"

MALE VS. FEMALE

When dogs were sent to space, the Soviet Union found that female dogs were the way to go. They found that male dogs had a very difficult time urinating in a collection device in a cramped capsule. The main challenge was because of how they normally urinate by lifting one leg. Female dogs didn't have the same difficulty, which is why they were sent into space and male dogs weren't.

After Alan Shepard, the first American in space, had to pee in his suit because there was no other solution, NASA designed a urine collection device that would only work for men. Creating a similar solution for women was a challenge that NASA couldn't or didn't want to figure out in the 1960s.[1]

PRIVATE SPACE TOILETS

It was only after NASA had developed a "sit-down" private toilet that women were recruited as astronauts and sent to space alongside the men. While the toilet issue wasn't the only reason NASA waited so long to send women astronauts, it was still a big factor.[2]

THERE IS NO MEN'S SIZE SMALL

NASA created three sizes for the urine collection device. These hose attachments designed to fit the male body were worn inside the EVA suit. To avoid embarrassing astronauts and any mishaps that could be caused by astronauts choosing a size Large when they are really a size Small, there is no size Small. These male-only devices only come in Large, X-Large, and XX-Large sizes.[3]

ASTRONAUT ADULT DIAPERS

The adult diaper wasn't widespread until a Japanese company introduced it for adults with incontinence in 1987. NASA uses MAGs, which stands for Maximum Absorbency Garment. These are off-the-shelf adult diapers. During their EVA training in the NBL, astronauts wear the adult diapers with tape, just like what you use for infants. During launches, re-entry, and spacewalks they wear the pull-on adult diapers.[4]

HIGHLY ABSORBANT

These maximum-absorbency garments are extremely efficient and can absorb up to 300 times an astronaut's weight in liquid. This makes it possible to only need to change the diaper every eight to ten hours while still allowing the astronaut to be somewhat comfortable.[5]

DIAPER PRACTICE

Before astronauts fly into space, NASA sends them home with some adult diapers to practice with. One of the most challenging things for astronauts is learning to pee in the diaper should the need arise—especially while lying down. They have been trained since children to not pee their pants, and that's a hard habit to reverse. So, they go home, put the diapers on and lay flat in their bathtubs to practice.[6]

RUSSIAN COSMONAUTS MIGHT NOT USE DIAPERS

Astronaut Samantha Cristoforetti, who spent a lot of time training in Russia alongside cosmonauts, has said that the cosmonauts might not wear adult diapers during launch, re-entry and possibly even spacewalks.[7]

TWO TOILETS ONBOARD THE ISS

There is one toilet in the Russian segment in the Zvezda module and one in Node 3 of the U.S. segment. A new toilet with major upgrades was sent to the ISS in October 2020 and has been installed and is now being tested. So, there are currently three toilets on the ISS, but they will slowly replace the one in Node 3 with the new one.

USING THE TOILET IN SPACE

Basically, the toilet used in space is like a big vacuum that uses air to pull waste into the appropriate containers. There's a hose for urine with different funnel attachments for men and women. There's also a seat on top of a container that astronauts can "sit" on for number two. Some things to remember when using the toilet: remember to flip on the fan so that waste is pulled where it needs to go. This rule applies to both the hose and the toilet seat. It's important to remember to open the toilet hatch—it's also been called the guillotine—to make your deposit, remember to aim, but even more important is to remember to close the hatch and make sure there isn't any "debris" that gets cut off and floats away.[8]

THE CURLING EFFECT

After over 50 years of sending humans into space, we have learned a few unique things about going to the bathroom without gravity. One fact that doesn't always make the news is that without gravity to help pull feces straight down, they tend to curl backward as they make their exit. Space waste management engineers know this and have to account for this when building space toilets so the curl doesn't clog up the system.[9]

SPACE POTTY TRAINING

Going to the toilet in space isn't like going on Earth, and it takes training and practice to make sure you're ready for the real thing. Astronauts do go through potty training at the Johnson Space Center in Houston.[10] To make sure they know how to align their body and know what proper aim feels like, there is a camera down in the hole. This allows them see if they are in the right position to hit the mark. They don't actually use the toilet for real with the camera on, it's more of a "dry run."[11]

SCHEDULED TOILET VISITS

Gravity plays a big part in letting the body know that it's time to use the bathroom. As liquid waste accumulates on the floor of the bladder it begins to stretch, and sends those familiar signals to the brain saying that it's time to go. The more the bladder is stretched, the more insistent the urge to go is.

But when gravity isn't involved, urine doesn't collect at the bottom of the bladder. Instead, surface tension causes the liquid to stick to the side of the bladder wall. It isn't until the bladder is almost completely full and the sides of the bladder begin to stretch that the signal to go is sent. By this time, the bladder may be too full and can press the urethra shut, making it very difficult to urinate.

This is why astronauts schedule regular visits to the toilet, even when they don't feel the normal urge to go.[12]

NEW AUTOMATIC ISS TOILET
In October 2020, the ISS finally got an updated space toilet. Instead of flipping a switch to turn the fan on that pulls liquid and waste down and into the appropriate containers, the fan starts automatically as

Universal Waste Managments System (UWMS)
NASA'S new space toilet

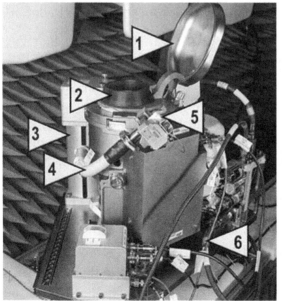

1. Lid
2. Seat
3. Urine preheat tank
4. Urine hose
5. Urine funnel attaches here (funnel not shown)
6. Urine Transfer System (UTS) attaches here

New toilet delivered to the ISS in October 2020. Photo courtesy of NASA.

soon as the toilet lid is lifted or the urine funnel is removed. This makes things smell a lot nicer and reduces the chance of any accidents happening if someone forgets to turn on the fan.[13]

DESIGNED WITH FEMALES IN MIND

The new ISS toilet was designed with female comfort in mind. Until now, space toilets had pee funnels and a seat for number two, but they couldn't be used at the same time—much to the dismay of female astronauts. With the new toilet, officially known as the Universal Waste Management System (UWMS), both waste-removal systems can be used simultaneously.

HOW NOT TO FLOAT AWAY WHILE YOU GO

Thigh straps have been used in the past to help keep astronauts in place and to prevent them floating off while they do their business. According to astronaut feedback, the thigh straps were a hassle and they asked for improvements. The new toilet now has foot restraints and handholds that allow the astronauts to better position themselves, but with less hassle.

LESS CLEAN-UP AND MAINTENANCE

Cleaning a toilet is not a fun job. Cleaning a toilet when things can escape and float away can be the stuff of nightmares! The new design is more ergonomic and requires much less cleanup and less time spent maintaining. Astronauts didn't sign up to be plumbers, but it is part of their job while on the International Space Station. So, the less time they have to spend on plumbing, the better.[14]

WASTE REMOVAL

The ISS toilet's solid-waste container is changed every 10 to 15 days.

A DIFFERENT KIND OF SHOOTING STAR

Solid-waste containers, used dirty clothes, empty food packaging and lightweight packing material like foam or bubble wrap is packed into a resupply cargo ship. This is then undocked at the end of the mission and burns up in Earth's atmosphere. Remember this the next time you see a shooting star in the sky! [15]

CRYSTALLIZED TRAIL OF PEE

Over the years—and before there was a water recovery system to recycle urine into drinkable water—much of the urine was released into space. The pee would immediately freeze into tiny crystals when it hit the cold vacuum of space. Believe it or not, flash-frozen urine sparkling in the sun has been described by multiple astronauts as one of the most beautiful sights in space. [16]

RECYCLING URINE AND SWEAT

The water recovery system onboard the ISS can take condensation, the crew's urine and even sweat and turn 90% of it into usable water. It takes about eight days to recycle, but the end result is purer than the water we drink from the tap in our own homes. This may sound nasty, but if we want to make it to Mars, recycling all available liquid is mission critical. Water is heavy and expensive to launch into orbit. It costs about $40,000 to launch a liter of water into orbit. So, it's important to recycle as much as possible. [17] We simply can't take all the water we would need for a three-year journey. [18] NASA's goal is to recycle 98% of available liquid and turn it into water. [19]

SOME ASTRONAUT WASTE IS SENT HOME TO STUDY

What happens to the body in space is of great interest to the scientists at home. Astronauts themselves are experiments, and they are studied and evaluated before, during and after their missions to space.

Something you may not have expected is that small amounts of astronaut fecal matter and urine are collected, saved and sent home. This has been done since astronauts have been going to the bathroom in space! On the top floor of a windowless high-security building at the Johnson Space Center in Houston, there are freezers with astronaut urine and feces samples that date back to the Skylab and Apollo days. [20]

NOTES

1. Mary Roach, *Packing for Mars: The Curious Science of Life in the Void* (New York, NY: WW Norton, 2011), 282.
2. Roach, *Packing for Mars*, 284.
3. Roach, *Packing for Mars*, 137.
4. "Clayton C. Anderson's Answer to Do Astronauts and Cosmonauts Get to Choose Which Brand of Adult Diapers They Wear While in Space? – Quora," Quora, accessed May 31, 2021, https://qr.ae/pGsOGu.
5. Tereza Pultarova, "Why Alan Shepard Had to Pee In His Space Suit," Space Safety Magazine, August 19, 2013, http://www.spacesafetymagazine.com/spaceflight/life-in-orbit/alan-shepard-pee-pants/.
6. Terry Virts, *How to Astronaut: An Insider's Guide to Leaving Planet Earth* (New York, Workman Publishing, 2020), 67-68.
7. Samantha Cristoforetti, *Diary of an Apprentice Astronaut*, trans. Jill Foulston (Penguin, 2020), 224, Kindle.
8. Virts, *How to Astronaut*, 125.
9. Roach, *Packing for Mars*, pg. 278.
10. Virts, *How to Astronaut*, 126.
11. Roach, *Packing for Mars*, 267-268.
12. Roach, *Packing for Mars*, 269.
13. Brian Dunbar, "Boldly Go! NASA's New Space Toilet," ed. Darcy Elburn, NASA (NASA, September 24, 2020), https://www.nasa.gov/feature/boldly-go-nasa-s-new-space-toilet-offers-more-comfort-improved-efficiency-for-deep-space/.
14. Dunbar, "Boldly Go!."
15. Tim Peake, *Ask an Astronaut: My Guide to Life in Space* (Little Brown and Company, 2017), 90.
16. Roach, *Packing for Mars*, 19.
17. Virts, *How to Astronaut*, 125.
18. Hilary Brueck, "A NASA Astronaut Who Spent 665 Days Circling the Planet Reveals the Misery of Going to the Bathroom in Space," Business Insider Australia, September 19, 2016, https://www.businessinsider.com.au/how-you-go-to-bathroom-space-nasa-astronaut-2018-5
19. Dunbar, "Boldly Go!."
20. Roach, *Packing for Mars*, 275.

LIVING IN WEIGHTLESSNESS

On Earth, we are used to the weight created by gravity to keep us on the planet. But as you get farther and farther away from Earth's surface, things start to change.

Microgravity NOT Zero Gravity

THERE IS STILL GRAVITY IN SPACE

Many people assume there is no gravity in space, but that's wrong. There is some degree of gravity everywhere in space. Gravity is the force that holds the Moon in orbit around the Earth, it's why the Earth orbits the Sun and it's why black holes attract all matter and energy.

The International Space Station is at an altitude of between 200 and 250 miles (320 to 400 km). At this altitude, the Earth's gravitational pull is only 10% weaker than it is on the Earth's surface.[1]

SO WHY ARE THEY FLOATING?

Even though there is still the pull of 90% of Earth's gravity onboard the International Space Station, things appear to float and become weightless. This is because everything is in free fall. The spaceship, the crew and everything inside are all falling towards the Earth, but they are all falling together at the same rate.

FALLING AROUND THE EARTH

Earth's gravity pulls on the space station and all other objects in orbit. But the ISS is also moving incredibly fast and at a speed that matches the curve of the Earth. This means that while the ISS is falling toward Earth, it's also moving around the curve of Earth fast enough to create an equilibrium. This creates the appearance of weightlessness of everything onboard and is how it stays in orbit at the same height.[2]

Here's what this looks like in numbers. The space station is moving at around 17,500 miles per hour (28,000 kilometers per hour), which is about 5 miles (8 km) per second. Every second in space, an astronaut drops toward Earth about 15 feet (5 meters). But at the same time, the astronaut moves forward 5 miles (8 km). Then the next second, the astronaut drops another 15 feet (5 meters) and moves forward another 5 miles (8 km). As long as an astronaut keeps traveling at that same speed, he or she will continue to circle the earth and keep a consistent altitude. This is how a person falls towards but also around the Earth.[3]

Training for Weightlessness
THE VOMIT COMET

One of the most effective ways to train for weightlessness is to experience weightlessness. To do that on Earth, astronauts and

Parabolic flight of the KC-135A NASA 930. Photo credit: NASA, Public domain, via Wikimedia Commons.

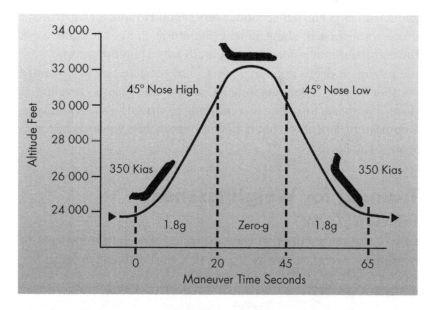

Flight trajectory for a typical zero gravity flight maneuver. Image credit: NASA, Public domain, via Wikimedia Commons.

cosmonauts will fly onboard planes that perform rollercoaster-like wave patterns with steep climbs and sharp dives. This is known as a parabolic pattern or Kepler curve. At the top hump of the wave, the plane and everything and everyone in it becomes weightless for about 25 seconds.

This movement is known to make about two-thirds of its passengers sick, which is where the "vomit comet" nickname came from. NASA prefers the name "weightless wonder" for obvious reasons.

Astronauts will fly up to 40 parabolas that last about 25 seconds each per flight. This allows them to train for different situations while weightless like performing emergency medical techniques or using unique equipment created for weightless environments.

WEIGHTLESSNESS MAKES SPACE TRAVEL IS EXPENSIVE

To be sure it works in microgravity, every new piece of equipment that goes up into space has to be tested on the Vomit Comet. This means every pump, fan, throttle, heating element and even space toilet gets a ride on the Weightless Wonder.[4]

FILMING SCENES FOR APOLLO 13 FILM

To make it as realistic as possible, the weightless scenes shot for the movie *Apollo 13* were filmed in NASA's KC-135 turbojet, aka the "Vomit Comet." Since weightlessness only lasts for about 23 to 25 seconds at a time, the scenes were broken down into small 25-second chunks. In the end, the *Apollo 13* cast and crew experienced 612 parabolas over 13 days with almost 4 hours of weightlessness. This is more than most astronauts in training get before flying into space.[5]

FLIP, FLOAT AND FLY LIKE ASTRONAUTS

Space Adventures, purchased Zero-G, an extreme tourism company that provides weightlessness experiences. Currently, an experience in their G-FORCE ONE, a modified Boeing 727-200, costs $6,700 + tax.[6] Total flight time is around 1.5 hours, during which passengers will experience 15 parabolas that provide around 25 seconds of weightlessness at a time. The total weightless experience will be between six and eight minutes.[7]

FLOAT LIKE COSMONAUTS

A Russian company called Migflug offers people the chance to "Float like Cosmonauts" on their IL-76, a wide body military airplane, at the price tag of 5,600 euros or about $6,800.[8]

FLOATING FAMOUS PEOPLE

In addition to Tom Hanks, Kevin Bacon and Bill Paxton, who got to experience weightlessness while filming *Apollo 13*, several other household names have also had the chance. *Titanic* director James Cameron, *Star Trek*'s George Takei, businessman Sir Richard Branson,[9] media mogul Martha Stewart, physicist Stephen Hawking and even Buzz Aldrin have experienced weightlessness in these large, modified airplanes.[10]

Astronauts and Cosmonauts train for spacewalks underwater. Photo
courtesy of NASA.

TRAINING FOR SPACEWALKS

Training for spacewalks in microgravity is done in the Neutral
Buoyancy Lab in Texas and in the Hydrolab in Star City, Russia. All
things Spacewalks is covered in the Spacewalk chapter.

Easy Things Become Hard

EATING TAKES LONGER

Food in space is packaged differently to make it space-friendly. But
even then, it can still take a long time to eat since gravity doesn't
help pull food down the esophagus.[11]

STAYING HYDRATED

Since body fluids shift and float towards the head in weightlessness,
an astronaut's sense of thirst is almost non-existent. This makes it a
constant challenge to stay hydrated.[12]

PUTTING SOCKS ON

According to astronaut Scott Kelly—who spent nearly a year in space— putting his socks on was one of the most challenging things to do without gravity to help him bend over.[13] Many astronauts find it's easier to pull their legs up and towards them to do this.[14]

LIP-READING IS HARD TO DO

We all lip read to some extent. Those who have been to space and have tried talking to someone who is upside-down discover it's difficult. Not because they are upside-down, but because their mouth is upside-down and that makes it difficult to visually match what they hear them saying.[15]

STANDING IN ONE PLACE

Astronauts are busy and have a lot of work they have to do while in space—especially onboard the ISS. Unfortunately, they can't just float around like Superman all day. But it turns out that staying still is actually harder than it sounds. Astronauts will often hook their toes under metal handrails, straps and bungees to hold themselves in place.[16]

EATING OFF A TABLE

Velcro strips and duct tape cover almost every surface of the International Space Station, including the "table" the crew uses to eat off of. They use these sticky materials to keep their dinner in place. But sometimes an astronaut's drink bag, spoon or cookie will escape and float away. Part of the dining experience in space includes reaching out and catching whatever part of anyone's dinner that might have floated off.[17]

GOING TO THE TOILET

Astronauts get to go through toilet training again before they head off into space. There is very specific training on not just how to use the toilet, but how to strap themselves to the toilet so they don't float away mid-stream.

PLEASE RESTRAIN EVERYTHING

It's something we don't ever think about here on Earth, but everything will float away if not properly stored and restrained in space. Several methods are used to keep things in their proper place: Velcro, bungee cords, straps, tethers, pockets, storage bags, containers and ziplock bags.[18]

Stuff You Use Differently in Microgravity

VELCRO & POCKETS

In space, everything floats everywhere and getting stuff to "stay put" is vital. Velcro and pockets are used a LOT in space, especially on the International Space Station. There are patches of Velcro placed

Astronaut Tom Marshburn onboard the ISS. Notice the Velcro strips on his pants.
Photo courtesy of NASA.

strategically on every wall and even on the crews' clothing. Even the items astronauts regularly use have matching Velcro. (To see for yourself, check out the Google Earth ISS photos and you'll noticed all of the Velcro on the walls.) Items shipped to the astronauts will also often come with their own Velcro dots pre-attached for convenience.[19]

The "table" astronauts use for eating has strategically placed Velcro strips and duct tape to help keep items in place.[20]

While pockets are handy on Earth, they are even more important when in microgravity. If you've ever watched the astronauts working while onboard the International Space Station, you'll notice they are wearing clothes with strips of Velcro attached to their thighs as well as lots of pockets.

NOSE SCRATCHER

Velcro has also been found inside spacesuit helmets to make it easy for astronauts to lean over and scratch their noses since they aren't able to do that the normal way in the bulky outfits.[21]

THERE IS NO UP OR DOWN

In microgravity, it doesn't matter what is up or down. Onboard the International Space Station you would find the water dispenser on what could be considered the ceiling, the crew quarters on the floor, and a treadmill on a wall. They literally can use all the space that is available to them because they aren't limited when it comes to gravity.[22]

MIRRORS

Mirrors are handy tools in space. Astronauts wear mirrors on their wrists during spacewalks to see switches and labels on the front of their suit that is normally out of view. Sometimes astronauts request a small mirror to be handy during launch and landing so they could use it to see things behind them or just out of view while strapped into their seats. Wearing spacesuits with helmets attached to the suit makes it difficult to see things so mirrors become valuable tools.[23]

The Body in Microgravity

HOT & SWEATY ASTRONAUTS

Sweat in microgravity evaporates much slower than it does on Earth. This makes it harder for astronauts to cool down—especially during workouts. Researchers have found that astronauts' resting body temperature onboard the ISS increases to about 100.4°F (38°C) over time. Considering that 98.6 °F (37°C) is average, this would make one hot astronaut! As you would imagine, astronauts get even hotter during their daily workouts when their body temperatures reach over 104°F (40°C).[24]

NO MORE RUNNY NOSES

While astronauts do get congested, they do not ever have to worry about a runny nose because there's no gravity pulling the snot down. So, in weightlessness, nothing runs, except maybe an astronaut on a space treadmill.[25]

TALLER ASTRONAUTS

Without gravity, the spine isn't compressed and will lengthen and straighten. Some astronauts become up to 2.5 inches (6.4 cm) taller while in space. But it's not a permanent growth spurt, and they return to their normal height once they're back on Earth.[26]

WASP WAIST

Astronauts lose about three inches (7.6 cm) from their waistline because their internal organs float upwards under their ribcage.[27] This can make it harder to breathe as deeply in space as they would be able to on Earth.

CHICKEN-LEG SYNDROME

Astronauts who spend a significant amount of time in space develop what some call "bird legs." Their legs, especially their calves, become thinner and thinner. This happens when blood and other fluids migrate towards the upper part of the body. Another contributing factor is the fact that muscle tissue is lost over time.[28]

FACES BECOME PUFFY AND SWOLLEN

In microgravity, body fluids shift from the lower part of the body to the upper part of the body. This can cause the face to look puffy and swollen.[29]

HIGH-CHEEK BONES & SQUINTY EYES

Loose flesh on the face will float upwards on the bone and cause a high-cheek bone effect with a slightly squinty eye appearance.[30]

HAVE TO USE THE BATHROOM MORE

Because the body's blood volume sensors are in the upper body, when the fluid shift happens your body thinks you're retaining too much fluid and will send signals to your body to correct it. Astronauts can lose 10% to 15% of water weight during the first few days in space.[31]

THE VOICE BECOMES NASALLY

The fluid shift can also cause astronauts' voices to take on a nasal tone.[32]

TO WEAR A BRA OR NOT TO WEAR A BRA, THAT IS THE QUESTION

Some women astronauts wear their bra in space and some don't. It's more of a personal preference than a support issue. In weightlessness, there isn't the same need for support like there is on Earth.[33]

Things Only There for Psychological Reasons

DINING TABLE

If you think about it, astronauts don't actually need a table to "sit down" at. But having a table on the International Space Station to sit around at the end of the day to eat and talk is familiar and is important for psychological reasons.

SIT-DOWN TOILETS

Sitting down to rid yourself of bodily waste is something that most of us have done for most of our lives. But astronauts have not always had the luxury of a sit-down toilet in space. After the Apollo program where the astronauts used fecal bags instead of a toilet, they *strongly* suggested that they physically and psychologically needed and wanted a sit-down toilet.[34]

SLEEPING BAG STRAPS

One of the things astronauts say they miss the most while in space is feeling the weight of the blanket against them while in bed. To simulate that, astronauts have straps that they can use to strap around their sleeping bags to provide some pressure. Astronaut straps also help keep their arms from floating up in front of them while they sleep. This can help prevent potential scares—both of themselves and fellow crewmembers—and prevents them from accidentally touching something in their sleep.

Mission Specialist Dale Gardner sleeps in sleep restraints while on the Space Shuttle Challenger in 1983. Photo courtesy of NASA.

RIGID CUSHION IN THEIR SLEEPING BAGS

Another item astronauts use to help simulate sleeping on Earth is a small rigid cushion. Inside the sleeping bag is a rigid cushion that puts pressure on the back to simulate sleeping on a mattress.[35]

PILLOWS

Without gravity, there really isn't a need to have a pillow while sleeping in space, but many astronauts still prefer them. To sleep with a pillow, which is really only a block of foam or clothes bunched up, they use Velcro to strap it to their head and keep it in place throughout the night.[36]

NOTES

1. Brian Dunbar, "What Is Microgravity?," ed. Sandra May, NASA (NASA, August 7, 2017), https://www.nasa.gov/audience/forstudents/5-8/features/nasa-knows/what-is-microgravity-58.html.

2. Dunbar, "What Is Microgravity?."

3. Terry Virts, *How to Astronaut: An Insider's Guide to Leaving Planet Earth* (New York, Workman Publishing, 2020), 83.

4. Mary Roach, *Packing for Mars: The Curious Science of Life in the Void* (New York, NY: WW Norton, 2011), 106.

5. Caroline Siede, "On Apollo 13's 20th Anniversary, a Look at How They Made the Film so Realistic," The A.V. Club, June 30, 2015, https://news.avclub.com/on-apollo-13-s-20th-anniversary-a-look-at-how-they-mad-1798281369.

6. "Zero Gravity Flight," Space Adventures, accessed May 31, 2021, https://spaceadventures.com/experiences/zero-gravity-flight/.

7. "FAQ," ZERO-G, accessed May 31, 2021, https://www.gozerog.com/faq/.

8. "Zero Gravity Flight in Russia with MiGFlug.com," MiGFlug, accessed May 31, 2021, https://migflug.com/flights-prices/zero-gravity-in-russia/.

9. Nola Taylor Redd, "Vomit Comet: Training Flights for Astronauts," Space.com, August 25, 2017, https://www.space.com/37942-vomit-comet.html.

10. "About Us - ZERO-G," ZERO-G, August 14, 2020, https://www.gozerog.com/about-us/.

11. Alexander Voss, "Racine Remembers a Hero: Laurel Clark Letter Home," Racine.wi.net, March 13, 2007, https://web.archive.org/web/20070313102022/http://racine.wi.net/clarkletter.html.

12. Voss, "Racine Remembers a Hero."

13. Scott Kelly, *Endurance: A Year in Space, A Lifetime of Discovery* (New York: Alfred A. Knopf, 2017), 76.

14. William R. Pogue, *How Do You Go to the Bathroom in Space?* (New York, NY: Tor, 1999), 26.

15. Roach, *Packing for Mars*, 114.
16. Tim Peake, *Ask an Astronaut: My Guide to Life in Space* (Little Brown and Company, 2017), 111.
17. Kelly, *Endurance*, 94.
18. Virts, *How to Astronaut*, 85.
19. Kelly, *Endurance*, 94.
20. Kelly, *Endurance*, 78.
21. Matt Soniak, "How Do Astronauts Scratch Their Noses on Space Walks?," Mental Floss, October 3, 2013, https://www.mentalfloss.com/article/52987/how-do-astronauts-scratch-their-noses-space-walks.
22. Samantha Cristoforetti, *Diary of an Apprentice Astronaut*, trans. Jill Foulston (Penguin, 2020), 261, Kindle.
23. *Behind the Scenes: Astronauts Pockets Deep in Mystery*, YouTube (NASA, 2013), https://www.youtube.com/watch?v=-pl37GnhpEs&t=763s.
24. Amber Jorgenson, "Space Causes Astronauts to Run Hot," Astronomy.com, January 8, 2018, https://astronomy.com/news/2018/01/space-causes-astronauts-to-run-hot.
25. R. Mike Mullane, *Do Your Ears Pop in Space? by R. Mike Mullane* (John Wiley & Sons, Inc: 1997), 76.
26. Virts, *How to Astronaut*, 232.
27. Pogue, *How Do You Go to the Bathroom in Space?*, 185.
28. Pogue, *How Do You Go to the Bathroom in Space?*, 23.
29. Roach, *Packing for Mars*, 103.
30. Pogue, *How Do You Go to the Bathroom in Space?*, 26.
31. Roach, *Packing for Mars*, 103.
32. Cristoforetti, *Diary of an Apprentice Astronaut*, 246.
33. Mullane, *Do Your Ears Pop in Space?*. 137.
34. Roach, *Packing for Mars*, 271.
35. "Sleeping in Space," CSA (Canadian Space Agency, August 22, 2019), https://www.asc-csa.gc.ca/eng/astronauts/living-in-space/sleeping-in-space.asp.
36. Leigh Devine, "Astronauts Sleep in Padded Broom Closets and Velcro Their Heads to Pillows," Business Insider, October 18, 2015, https://www.businessinsider.com/how-astronauts-sleep-in-space-2015-10.

ASTRONAUTS AS EXPERIMENTS

IT MAY BE URINE TO YOU, BUT IT'S GOLD FOR US

We don't normally think about it, but a lot of important data can be extracted from fecal matter and urine. So, when humans go to space, getting as much data about the experience is very important. As one NASA researcher put it, "It may be urine to you, but it's gold for us."[1]

In Houston, Texas, on the top floor of a windowless high-security building at the Johnson Space Center, there are freezers with astronaut urine and feces samples from the Skylab and Apollo days.[2]

Even now, astronauts still send waste samples back to Earth on spacecraft headed home because there is still a lot of valuable data that can be found in these special samples. Researchers can learn a lot about an astronaut's nutrition and how their diet affects their health from studying the waste samples. This then helps inform future space food choices. So, look out for those bio samples onboard returning SpaceX Dragons.[3]

BLOOD & SALIVA SAMPLES

It isn't just about the urine and feces, astronaut blood and saliva is also a goldmine for science. Many of the experiments that astronauts participate in require blood and saliva samples in order to measure and analyze differences between the blood and saliva samples they provided on Earth. Often, they are asked to provide more samples when they return to Earth to see if any differences return to the same pre-space levels.

SHOW ME YOUR MUSCLES

Over the years, we've learned that microgravity isn't good for muscle mass and muscle strength. Several experiments are underway to counteract those effects. In order to get the right data, some muscle mass experiments require a small biopsy of the calf muscle before and after space missions.[4]

HAIR TELLS A STORY

The hair study collects five pieces of hair, including the root, from ISS crew members. Using the hair, researchers can analyze the body's stress levels and see if any metabolic changes have occurred due to microgravity or radiation.

TAKING ULTRASOUNDS OF EACH OTHER

As part of an Ultrasound in Microgravity experiment, astronauts perform ultrasounds on each other. They are trying to determine how accurate an ultrasound would be in evaluating and diagnosing roughly 250 specific types of injuries, illnesses or in-flight bone changes. Astronauts take scans of the heart, lungs, liver, kidneys, bladder, eyes, sinuses and different bones.[5]

COMFORT FOOD IN SPACE

Space is stressful, and researchers are looking for ways to reduce stress while helping crew members cope and improve their mood. On Earth, eating food that is comforting is one way many of us cope with stress. Does this work in space? There's currently an ISS experiment to find out. Please pass the chocolate pudding![6]

THE BRAIN IN SPACE

By taking MRI brain scans of the astronauts before they go to space and then when they return to Earth, researchers have measured the brain's plasticity, or how quickly astronauts' brains adapted to new inputs. Fortunately, the study showed that their brains adapted surprisingly well.[7]

EYE SEE YOU

Astronauts wore a special device that tracked their eye movements throughout the day as they performed various activities. The same technology used in these experiments are now commonly used to track a patient's eye during laser eye surgery to precisely direct the laser scalpel.[8]

CAN YOU HEAR ME NOW?

To measure the effects of microgravity and the continuous noise in ISS, astronauts have their hearing checked before, during and after their mission.[9]

TESTING LONG-DURATION SPACE UNDERWEAR

In May 2009, JAXA astronaut Koichi Wakata was tasked with performing an experiment where he did not change his special long-duration space underwear for the entire month he was in space. The experiment was to test the odor-repelling properties of the garment. His crewmates never complained, so the experiment is being called a success.[10]

THE ASTRORAD RADIATION VEST

Astronauts are testing a new vest called the AstroRad, designed to protect the wearer from radiation while living on the ISS. They wear it to bed, during daily activities, while exercising and while eating. They are testing to see how comfortable it is, if it limits movement, if it disrupts their sleep and how easy or hard it is to put on and remove.[11]

THE NASA TWINS STUDY

Identical twin brothers Scott and Mike Kelly both became astronauts. This gave NASA the opportunity to compare the impact of long-duration space travel on humans, since these brothers share the exact same DNA. Scott Kelly spent nearly a year in space. His brother, Mark Kelly, stayed home. Multiple experiments have been performed before, during the mission and after returning to Earth.[12]

Results have shown that most of the changes that happened in space returned to the way they were before Scott left, showing that the body is able to adapt and adjust. But there was some minor damage to his DNA and drops in his mental performance that haven't returned back exactly the way they were before.[13] [14]

Scott and Mike Kelly are identical twins and are both astronauts. Photo courtesy of NASA/Bill Ingalls

A FLU SHOT IN SPACE

Scott Kelly received three flu shots, each one year apart. One before he went to space, one while he was in space and one when he got home. Findings showed that Scott's body reacted appropriately to the vaccine, which leads scientists to believe that our immune systems respond the way they should even in space.[15]

KEEPING SPACE JOURNALS

Explorers have often kept journals that give us a lot of information about their experiences—especially how they coped with difficult situations and harsh environments. Most ISS astronauts have participated in an experiment called Journals since the first crew launched in 2000. They write or record audio about their dreams, if they dream or if they don't, how they feel, what they worry about and other things you'd write about in a journal on Earth.[16] Among other things, these journals have helped researchers learn more about how humans work in extreme environments, isolation and confinement.[17]

NOTES

1. Tariq Malik, "Blood and Astronaut Pee: Creepy Cargo Returns to Earth on SpaceX Capsule Today," Space.com, October 28, 2012, https://www.space.com/18253-astronaut-blood-urine-spacex-dragon-capsule.html.

2. Mary Roach, *Packing for Mars: The Curious Science of Life in the Void* (New York, NY: WW Norton, 2011), 275.

3. Malik, "Blood and Astronaut Pee."

4. "Effect of Prolonged Space Flight on Human Skeletal Muscle," Space Station Research Explorer on NASA.gov (NASA), accessed May 31, 2021, https://www.nasa.gov/mission_pages/station/research/experiments/explorer/Investigation.html#id=238.

5. "Advanced Diagnostic Ultrasound in Microgravity," Space Station Research Explorer on NASA.gov (NASA), accessed May 31, 2021, https://www.nasa.gov/mission_pages/station/research/experiments/explorer/Investigation.html#id=129.

6. "Factors Contributing to Food Acceptability and Consumption, Mood and Stress on Long-Term Space Missions," Space Station Research Explorer on NASA.gov (NASA), accessed May 31, 2021, https://www.nasa.gov/mission_pages/station/research/experiments/explorer/Investigation.html#id=1127.

7. European Space Agency, "20 Top Experiments From 20 Years of Human Research on the International Space Station," SciTechDaily, November 4, 2020, https://scitechdaily.com/20-top-experiments-from-20-years-of-human-research-on-the-international-space-station/.

8. "Eye-Catching Space Technology Restoring Sight," ESA (European Space Agency), accessed May 31, 2021, https://www.esa.int/Science_Exploration/Human_and_Robotic_Exploration/Research/Eye-catching_space_technology_restoring_sight.

9. "Acoustic Upgraded Diagnostics In-Orbit," Space Station Research Explorer on NASA.gov (NASA), accessed May 31, 2021, https://www.nasa.gov/mission_pages/station/research/experiments/explorer/Investigation.html#id=7898.

10. Tariq Malik, "Japanese Space Underwear Keeps Stink Out," Space.com, July 30, 2009, https://www.space.com/7077-japanese-space-underwear-stink.html.

11. "Comfort and Human Factors: AstroRad Radiation Garment Evaluation (CHARGE)," Space Station Research Explorer on NASA.gov (NASA), accessed May 31, 2021, https://www.nasa.gov/mission_pages/station/research/experiments/explorer/Investigation.html#id=7803.

12. Brian Dunbar, "NASA's Twins Study Results Published in Science Journal," ed. Jason Perez, NASA (NASA, last modified February 6, 2020), https://www.nasa.gov/feature/nasa-s-twins-study-results-published-in-science.

13. Rachel Becker, "Getting Scott Kelly's Blood Back to Earth Was a Logistical Nightmare," The Verge (The Verge, April 11, 2019), https://www.theverge.com/2019/4/11/18306653/scott-kelly-blood-earth-logistics-nasa-twins-study-international-space-station.

14. Francine E. Garrett-Bakelman et al., "The NASA Twins Study: A Multidimensional Analysis of a Year-Long Human Spaceflight," Science 364, no. 6436 (November 2019), https://science.sciencemag.org/content/364/6436/eaau8650.

15. Dunbar, "NASA Twins Study Results."

16. Scott Kelly, Endurance: A Year in Space, A Lifetime of Discovery (New York: Alfred A. Knopf, 2017), 165.

17. Melissa Gaskill, "12 Cool Experiments Done on the International Space Station," Mental Floss, October 27, 2014, https://www.mentalfloss.com/article/59639/12-cool-experiments-done-international-space-station.

WEIRD SPACE AILMENTS, INJURIES & ILLNESSES

Only in Space
SPACE BRAIN
Symptoms of "space brain" include difficulty concentrating, forgetting easily, not noticing things happening and not being able to think of solutions as quickly as you could back on Earth. The body does adjust, but space brain seems to be most noticeable in the first few days and weeks in space.[1][2]

NERVE PAIN
Without gravity pushing down and compressing the spine, astronauts will grow a few inches while in space. When this happens, the nerves and muscles stretch to try and keep up with the sudden growth spurt. The nerves and muscles stretch at different rates and can cause shooting nerve pain in astronauts feet and other parts of the body.[3]

LIZARD FEET
Astronauts develop what they call "lizard feet" on the tops of their toes. This isn't necessarily an injury, but it's something unique that happens while in space. Since there's no gravity, astronauts need to stabilize their body positions while working. To do that, they use their toes to hook their feet underneath metal handrails, straps and bungees. Because of this unusual activity, the skin on the tops of their toes becomes rough and scaly.

Experimental socks are being designed to help prevent this from happening. The socks have a soft rubber coating over the top of the toes and seem to be helping with the issue.[4]

FLAKY FOOT SKIN

Since astronauts rarely use the soles of their feet while in space, there is barely any weight on them. So, their soles become soft and smooth, much like the feet of a newborn baby. On Earth, we naturally build up hard skin and calluses on the soles of our feet. When that's not needed to protect the feet anymore, that hard skin starts to flake off. In space, nothing sinks to the ground, so dead skin flakes will float around until the airflow pulls them into one of the many air filters. Taking your socks off carefully in space is a must.[5]

Space Sickness

SPACE ADAPTATION SYNDROME, AKA SPACE SICKNESS

This special type of motion sickness can cause dizziness, headaches, insomnia and nausea.

Between 60%-80% of astronauts and cosmonauts will experience space sickness during the first couple of days in space. It doesn't matter if they have had hundreds of flight hours in other high-flying vehicles, it can still happen.

TECHNICALLY IT'S NOT A SICKNESS

Motion sickness is actually the body's normal response to an abnormal situation. It just happens to affect some people harder and faster than others.

OTHER SPECIES GET MOTION SICKNESS

Fish, monkeys, chimps, seals, sheep, cats, dogs and some birds can get motion sickness and will vomit. Horses and cows can become nauseated, but are unable to vomit due to anatomical differences. The only mammals thought to be immune are guinea pigs and rabbits.[6]

THE ONLY GROUP OF PEOPLE WHO ARE IMMUNE

Research has shown that people who are deaf and have nonfunctioning inner ears, or cochlea, are the only ones who are predictably immune to motion sickness. The cochlea is the part of the inner ear that regulates your balance. The disconnect between the signals your ears and eyes are sending to your brain while in space creates motion sickness.

EXPENSIVE VOMIT BAGS

Vomiting, puking, barfing or throwing up—whatever you call it, it's a tricky business in space. Without gravity, vomit bounces back off the other side of the barf bag. So, NASA has gone to great lengths to create a bag that makes this nasty business as hassle-free as possible.

These special space vomit bags have a big washcloth sewn onto then with an integrated twist tie. This makes it easy and convenient to open the bag, do what you gotta do, wipe yourself off, tightly seal the bag and throw it away in a safe place. These fancy vomit bags cost about $500 each. I'm sure the astronauts who need them feel they are worth every penny.[9]

CAN CAUSE INSOMNIA

Dizziness and nausea can make it hard to sleep. Sleeping can already be tricky in space, so having extra issues isn't helpful. NASA has astronauts take a common nausea medication called promethazine, sold under the name of Phenergan.[10] It's typically used to prevent nausea caused by things like morning sickness, post-chemo nausea, and motion sickness. Apparently, it works wonders and helps astronauts get the much-needed relief and sleep they need.[11]

THE GARN SCALE

Jake Garn was the first US senator to fly into space, which occurred in 1985. He had hundreds of hours of flight-time experience as a Navy combat pilot. But even with that extensive flight-time, he suffered from space sickness the majority of his week-long space shuttle flight. NASA later came up with an informal scale to measure the severity of space sickness named the "Garn scale." On this scale, one Garn is the most extreme sick someone can be. Most astronauts will only get to 1/10th of a Garn.[12]

SPACE SICKNESS WHEN COMING HOME

When astronauts return home, their inner ears have to adjust to gravity again. This means that space sickness can happen for several days after being back on Earth.

CAN GET IT EVERY TIME

Just because you've been to space once doesn't mean you can't get space sickness again. Some people have to readjust every time they go into space.[13]

SEEING SOMEONE UPSIDE DOWN CAN BE HAZARDOUS

During the time when astronauts were on the Spacelab space station, lots of research was done on space motion sickness. Charles Oman, resident motion sickness expert at the National Space Biomedical Research Institute said, "Several Spacelab crew described sudden vomiting episodes after seeing a nearby crew member floating upside down." [14]

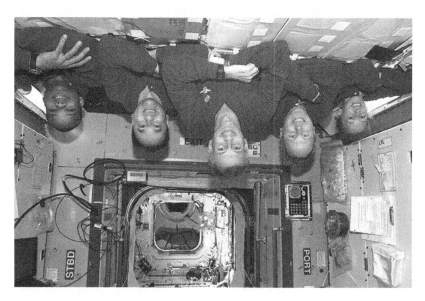

Upside-down or right-side up astronauts? The crew of STS-98 take a break on the ISS. Photo courtesy of NASA.[15]

TRICKS TO ADJUST

Over the years, astronauts have come up with things to do while still on Earth to help them adjust as quickly as possible to space sickness. One is to raise one end of a mattress a few centimeters and lie with the feet elevated. Another trick is to lie on a table tilted at a 45-degree angle with your head down.[16]

Everything Else

SPACE GLOVES CAUSE LOST FINGERNAILS

As of 2022, the pressurized gloves astronauts currently wear during spacewalks can cause fingernail trauma. This eventually leads to fingernails falling off after using the gloves in space. Some astronauts will remove their fingernails before going on a spacewalk to save them from some serious pain later and the danger of the nails getting snagged inside the gloves. New glove designs are in the works to prevent this from happening in the future.[17]

OTHER SKIN INJURIES

Skin problems among the astronauts on the ISS are the most common issue. They include dry skin, rashes, red spots, eczema and general discomfort.[18]

HIGH LEVELS OF CO_2

Astronauts are humans, and just like humans on Earth they exhale CO_2. On Earth we have plants that take that CO_2 and convert it into sugar and oxygen. In space, astronauts must rely on CO_2 scrubbers onboard the ISS. These scrubbers are a combination of American and Russian machines and are able to keep the CO_2 levels around 3mm HG of partial pressure. This level is more than 10 times what we have on Earth.[19]

LEARNING WHAT EXCESSIVE CO_2 FEELS LIKE

With CO_2 levels higher than what they're used to, astronauts need to learn how their bodies react to high levels of CO_2 so they can do something about it before it becomes dangerous. Early symptoms can include headaches, dizziness, increased blood pressure, tiredness, space brain, sleep difficulties and increased irritability.[20]

According to astronaut Terry Virts, the way he learned what his individual symptoms were for excessive CO_2 was with this simple test NASA came up with. They put bags over the astronauts' faces and had them breathe until the CO_2 built up and they began to feel dizzy.[21] Please don't try this at home!

LONG-TERM EFFECTS
Currently, long-term effects of high levels of CO_2 are unknown, but it's something researchers are looking into as astronauts are in space for longer and longer periods of time.

GETTING THE BENDS
There is a risk of an astronaut getting decompression sickness, also known as the bends, during a spacewalk. It's all about the amount of air pressure. The pressure inside the American EVA spacesuit is 4.3 psi, which is about one-third of an atmosphere and lower than what we're used to. To put this into perspective, this is lower than the pressure at the summit of Mt. Everest, which is 4.89 psi.

The low pressure in the suit allows the astronaut to move around in the big bulky pressurized suit. The pressure is kept just above the point where dissolved nitrogen in the body can start to form tiny bubbles and cause the bends.

To decrease the risk of getting decompression sickness, astronauts flush as much nitrogen out of the body as possible before their spacewalk. They breathe 100% oxygen and depressurize the airlock to 10.2 psi while getting dressed for their EVA. Doing light exercises for 50 minutes while suited at this pressure helps wash out as much nitrogen from the blood and body tissue as possible. This helps them reduce the risk of getting the bends. While out performing their spacewalks, they breathe 100% oxygen, which also helps.[22]

The Russian Orlan spacesuit has an air pressure of 5.8 psi as opposed to 4.3 psi in the American spacesuit. This means that the suit is much stiffer and harder to move around and work in, but it makes it less likely that the cosmonaut will get decompression sickness.[23]

SUITS CAN BE USED AS DECOMPRESSION CHAMBERS

If an astronaut were to get the bends while on an EVA, they would be helped back into the space station by the other astronaut. Spacewalks are always done in pairs for safety reasons.

Once inside the space station, the astronaut would be kept inside their spacesuit. Under the guidance of the flight surgeon, the pressure inside the suit would be increased above the space station's normal atmosphere to allow the bubbles of nitrogen gas to dissolve back into the body. They would then slowly reduce the air pressure to normal. Basically, they'd be using the spacesuit as a personal decompression chamber.[24]

As of June 2022, there have been no reports of astronauts or cosmonauts suffering from decompression sickness while in space.

SINUS CONGESTION

Without gravity, fluids shift from the lower part of the body to the upper part of the body. This can cause swelling in the face as well as sinus congestion. Many astronauts experience sinus congestion during spaceflight and use over-the-counter medicines to help.

CHANGES IN TASTE

It's thought that the fluid shift that can cause sinus congestion can also change and dampen an astronaut's taste. Astronauts who usually dislike spicy foods on Earth can't get enough of them in space. For example, shrimp cocktail coated with a spicy horseradish sauce is one of the most popular dishes onboard the ISS. Astronauts say a lot of the food onboard tastes bland, so any condiment that adds spice or tang is highly coveted.[25]

VISION PROBLEMS

Another problem that seems to happen due to the fluid shift in microgravity is that the extra fluid in the head puts more pressure on the optic nerve and eyeballs. This is referred to as spaceflight-associated neuro-ocular syndrome or SANS. Just under half of astronauts who spend a significant amount of time in space experience changes in their eyesight. For some astronauts, these problems go away once they return to Earth, but a few have reported that the changes are permanent.[26]

LOSING BONE & MUSCLE MASS

In the 1980s and 1990s, while cosmonauts were on the space station Mir, researchers learned that cosmonauts would lose 1% to 1.5% bone mass per month while in space. Not only did they lose bone density, but they also lost muscle mass—especially in their lower body.[27] To counteract these significant effects, all cosmonauts and astronauts are required to exercise at least six days a week for at least two hours a day.

Each astronaut and cosmonaut has a custom-made workout program of cardio and strength training to help them maintain muscle, bone and heart function while in space.[28]

NOTES

1. Terry Virts, *How to Astronaut: An Insider's Guide to Leaving Planet Earth* (New York, Workman Publishing, 2020), 87.

2. Scott Kelly, *Endurance: A Year in Space, A Lifetime of Discovery* (New York: Alfred A. Knopf, 2017), 226.

3. Virts, *How to Astronaut*, 232.

4. Tim Peake, *Ask an Astronaut: My Guide to Life in Space* (Little Brown and Company, 2017), 111.

5. Peake, *Ask an Astronaut*, 110.

6. Mary Roach, *Packing for Mars: The Curious Science of Life in the Void* (New York, NY: WW Norton, 2011), 121, 123.

7. Roach, *Packing for Mars*, 123.

8. Brian Dunbar, "How Deaf and Hearing Impaired People Helped the Space Program," NASA (NASA, July 22, 2011), https://www.nasa.gov/stem-ed-resources/TSD_Helped-SP_Video.html.

9. Virts, *How to Astronaut*, 228.

10. NASA "NASA Emergency Medical Procedures Manual for the ISS [partial], 2016," Governmentattic.org, March 21, 2016, https://www.governmentattic.org/19docs/NASA-ISSmedicalEmergManual_2016.pdf.

11. Virts, *How to Astronaut*, 229.

12. Robert E. Stevenson, "Oral History," interview by Carol Butler, May 13, 1999, interview transcript, Johnson Space Center History Collection, NASA, https://historycollection.jsc.nasa.gov/JSCHistoryPortal/history/oral_histories/StevensonRE/StevensonRE_5-13-99.htm.

13. Kelly, *Endurance*, 224

14. Roach, *Packing for Mars*, 114.

15. "STS-98 crew takes a break in the U.S. Laboratory/Destiny module," NASA, February 15, 2001, photograph, https://images.nasa.gov/details-s98e5284.

16. Samantha Cristoforetti, *Diary of an Apprentice Astronaut*, trans. Jill Foulston (Penguin, 2020), 215, Kindle.

17. Victoria Jaggard, "Astronauts' Fingernails Falling Off Due to Glove Design," National Geographic, May 3, 2021, https://www.nationalgeographic.com/news/2010/9/100913-science-space-astronauts-gloves-fingernails-injury/.

18. Virts, *How to Astronaut*, 123.

19. Virts, *How to Astronaut*, 12-13.

20. Heather Goss, "Why Living in Space Can Be a Pain in the Head," Air & Space Magazine, May 20, 2014, https://www.airspacemag.com/daily-planet/why-living-space-can-be-pain-head-180951507/.

21. Virts, *How to Astronaut*, 87.

22. Virts, *How to Astronaut*, 200.

23. Peake, *Ask an Astronaut*, 154.

24. Peake, *Ask an Astronaut*, 150.

25. Jim Romanoff, "When It Comes to Living in Space, It's a Matter of Taste," Scientific American, March 10, 2009, https://www.scientificamerican.com/article/taste-changes-in-space/.

26. "Robert Frost's Answer to Has Anyone on the Space Station Had Their Vision Checked to See If There Has Been an Increase or Decrease in Their Sight or Any Other Senses That Have Been Increased or Decreased at All Due to the Anti-Gravity? – Quora," Quora, accessed May 31, 2021, https://qr.ae/pNq5Jg.

27. Virts, *How to Astronaut*, 51.

28. "Getting a Jump on Astronaut Fitness," ESA (European Space Agency), accessed May 31, 2021, http://www.esa.int/Science_Exploration/Human_and_Robotic_Exploration/Getting_a_jump_on_astronaut_fitness.

BODY BAGS, DENTAL EQUIPMENT AND DEFIBRILLATORS, OH MY!

In Case of Emergencies

TRAINED FOR EMERGENCIES

While it's true that some astronauts were medical doctors before becoming astronauts, there's no guarantee that one of them will be in space when you need one. All astronauts are trained to handle many medical emergencies and routine injuries. They learn to mostly stabilize and restrain an injured astronaut and then call ground support to talk to the flight surgeons.

TYPES OF TRAINING

Astronauts learn many basic procedures, including CPR, how to insert chest tubes and perform a tracheotomy, how to administer life-saving drugs, how to give injections and how to use a defibrillator and respiratory support equipment. They also learn how to take blood—even their own! They can stitch sutures and treat a collapsed lung.[1] Some astronauts learn by spending time in hospital emergency rooms, learning how to identify symptoms and treat people accordingly. They even learn how to perform and take care of a few types of dental emergencies.

DENTAL PROCEDURES

Dental emergencies are a big deal. All astronauts learn how to do basic things like remove a tooth, replace a filling, how to treat tooth pain, replace a dental crown and do nerve blocks. American astronaut Terry Virts became the first to replace a crewmate's filling while in space.[2]

CPR CAN BE TRICKY

Chest compressions are one of the main components to CPR. On Earth, we are taught to use our own body weight to provide pressure. In microgravity, this method won't work. Plus, trying to do chest compressions on someone who is also floating can be tricky.

On the ISS there is a CPR bench firmly fixed to the deck of the Lab with straps for restraining both the person receiving CPR and the one performing CPR.[3]

THE HEIMLICH MANEUVER

Thankfully, the Heimlich maneuver is performed the same way in space as it is on Earth. Abdominal thrusts don't need gravity to be effective.

PROJECTITLE SPACE NEEDLES

If an astronaut is suffering from shock or severe respiratory failure, crew members are instructed to give an intraosseous injection directly into the patient's bone. But in microgravity, this can be tricky and comes with warnings in the ISS Emengency Medical Procedures Manual. Who knew astronauts had to be prepared for projectile needles?[4]

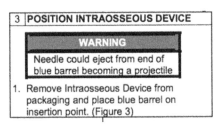

Figure 3.- Positioning Intraosseous Device.

Selection taken from the NASA Emergency Medical Procedures Manual for the ISS, 2016

ULTRASOUNDS

Astronauts use a small ultrasound unit onboard the ISS to examine crewmates' eyes, heart, lungs, blood vessels and abdomens. These scans can be part of experiments, or to examine an injured crew member. Ultrasounds use fluids to conduct the sound waves that bounce off your organs and echo back to the sensor to make an image. On Earth, the conducting fluid is a Vaseline-like gel that can be messy. In space, a blob of water works and is far less messy.[5]

MONTHLY CHECK-UPS

Astronauts and cosmonauts on the ISS perform monthly check-ups on each other. They take pictures of the eardrums, draw blood, and take temperatures and blood pressure.[6]

Inside the ISS Medicine Cabinet

PREPARED FOR EVERYTHING

To make sure the crew onboard the ISS has any medications needed, there is a well-stocked medicine "cabinet." Pretty much anything you'd find in a hospital emergency room you could find onboard the ISS.

Antibiotics, space motion sickness and anti-nausea meds, altitude sickness meds, pain relievers, decongestants, antihistamines, antidepressants, hormone treatments, allergy EpiPens and sleep meds are among the medications you'd find onboard the ISS.[7]

NASA likes to be prepared for everything, so there is also an early pregnancy test and a body bag onboard.[8]

COLOR-CODED ISS MEDICAL KITS

To keep things simple and organized, the medical kits onboard the ISS are color-coded. Here's a list of the medical kits you'd find and their associated colors.

White Convenience Medication Pack
Red Emergency Medical Treatment Pack
Gray Supply Pack
Blue Medical Diagnostic Pack
Green Medical Supply Pack
Pink Minor Treatment Pack
Purple Oral Medication Pack
Yellow Physician Equipment Pack
Brown Topical & Injectable Medication Pack

SLEEP MEDS

Onboard the ISS, astronauts have access to melatonin, zaleplon (brand name Sonata), and zolpidem (Ambien) to help them sleep.

STAY AWAKE MEDS

Caffeine onboard the ISS comes in a few different forms. Astronauts can sip a cup of coffee and tea. Or they can take it in pill form with Vivarin and Modafinil (Provigil).[9] Some astronauts have even brought 5-hour energy drinks onboard for special events like spacewalks.[10]

EVEN ASTRONAUTS GET DEPRESSED

Space isn't an easy place to live—far from friends, family and solid ground. Losing it in space is a serious danger. To help astronauts cope with psychological stress, the ISS stocks antipsychotics, antidepressants and anti-anxiety pills. Here are some of the medications onboard that would help: aripiprazole (brand name Abilify), lorazepam (Ativan), sertraline (Zoloft), and venlafaxine (Effexor).

NATURE'S TEARS & OTHER KINDS OF LUBE

Five different kinds of lubrication products can be found in the medical kits on the ISS: surgical, intranasal, and three brands of eyeball lubricant. Interestingly, one of those eye lube products is called "Nature's Tears," which is meant to artificially simulate your natural tears.

BIRTH CONTROL FOR FEMALE ASTRONAUTS

It's not for what you might be thinking. Norgestrel and ethinyl estradiol (brand name Ogestrel) are both available in 21-tablet packs on the ISS. Ogestrel is a hormone-based medication that is often used as birth control, but can also be used to allow women to skip their periods under doctor supervision.

Using the toilet in space is tricky enough, so most female astronauts work with their flight surgeons to avoid periods while in space.

NASA'S ISS MEDICAL EMERGENCY MANUAL

For those who wanted to know exactly what drugs and supplies NASA has onboard the ISS, this medical emergency manual contains just that, plus instructions for how to perform a limited number of emergency procedures. Find it at: https://www.governmentattic. org/19docs/NASA-ISSmedicalEmergManual_2016.pdf

TRIED AND TESTED AT HOME

To make sure no adverse reactions to medications happen while in space, NASA has astronauts try many of these stocked medications at home. NASA likes to be prepared and doesn't want to leave anything to chance, including allergic reactions or harmful interactions with other medications the astronaut might be taking.[11]

NO SPACE SURGERIES

As of June 2022, no astronaut has had a major injury or needed surgery in space. But as space exploration advances, the likelihood of that happening increases.

Dying in Space

DEATHS IN SPACE

As of June 2022, there have only been three deaths in space: three men onboard the Soyuz 11 spacecraft. After a three-week stay onboard space station Salyut 1, the crew onboard Soyuz 11 undocked to begin their journey back to Earth on June 29, 1971. A faulty seal burst open on the Soyuz during separation and the crew all died within seconds as the pressure and air were released into space. The Soyuz 11 landed successfully on autopilot back on Earth, but the crew were found dead from suffocation.

With exploration pushing farther and farther into space, the possibility of more humans dying in space increases.

If someone were to die in space there are basically two ways to deal with the body. One would be a type of burial at sea. The other option would be to return the body to the family back on Earth. Both options would be discussed among the crew, the crewmember's family and ground control back on Earth.

BODY BAGS

Because astronauts and cosmonauts have to be prepared for anything, there are body bags stored on the International Space Station in case a crew member dies while in space.[12]

BURIAL AT SEA

The ocean and space are similar in many ways. We use ships with crews on the oceans and spaceships with crews in space. To simulate the microgravity in space, astronauts train underwater. Navigating in space and at sea can be done using the sun and stars. Those who die at sea are often buried at sea. So, it makes sense that those who die in space would be "buried in space."

The burial at sea option would mean taking the body and sending it off into space. This could happen a few different ways. One would be to have crewmembers take the body into the airlock, open the airlock, then slowly push their deceased crewmate away from the space station and into the black sea of space.

The other option would be to send the body outside alone through the equipment airlock. The body would then be released robotically, the same way small satellites are launched. The body might be sent floating towards the Earth, where it would eventually burn up in the atmosphere and become a shooting star. Or the body would be sent floating away from Earth into outer space.[13]

RETURNING THE BODY TO EARTH

If it is decided that the body should be returned to Earth, a few options are possible. One option would be to send it home with crew members in a returning spaceship. The other option would be in a cargo ship that would splash down and be retrieved.

COMING BACK WITH THE CREW

If the body comes back with the crew this would mean dressing the body in its launch/entry suit, strapping the deceased astronaut into the proper seat in the space ship that would then return to Earth with other crew members.

SPECIAL CARGO IN THE CARGO VEHICLE

Sending the body home in a cargo vehicle is perhaps the safest and least awkward of all of the options. This way, the returning crew doesn't have to sit next to a deceased crewmember while they sit in their normal seats in the crewed capsule.[14]

NOTES

1. Samantha Cristoforetti, *Diary of an Apprentice Astronaut*, trans. Jill Foulston (Penguin, 2020), 321, Kindle.

2. Terry Virts, *How to Astronaut: An Insider's Guide to Leaving Planet Earth* (New York, Workman Publishing, 2020), 43.

3. Cristoforetti, *Diary of an Apprentice Astronaut*, 321.

4. NASA "NASA Emergency Medical Procedures Manual for the ISS [partial], 2016," Governmentattic.org, March 21, 2016, https://www.governmentattic.org/19docs/NASA-ISSmedicalEmergManual_2016.pdf.

5. Virts, *How to Astronaut*, 42.

6. Cristoforetti, *Diary of an Apprentice Astronaut*, 322.

7. Governmentattic.org, "NASA Emergency Medical Procedures Manual."

8. Scott Kelly, *Endurance: A Year in Space, A Lifetime of Discovery* (New York: Alfred A. Knopf, 2017), 337.

9. Governmentattic.org, "NASA Emergency Medical Procedures Manual."

10. Virts, *How to Astronaut*, 58.

11. Virts, *How to Astronaut*, 56-57.

12. Virts, *How to Astronaut*, 153.

13. Virts, *How to Astronaut*, 152-153.

14. Virts, *How to Astronaut*, 154.

MUSIC IN SPACE

Wake Up Music

THE FIRST WAKE-UP CALL

In the early days of the space program, the flights were often very short and there wasn't a need to send a wake-up call. The earliest recorded wake-up call was in December 1965 on the Gemini VI mission. A special personalized parody of "Hello Dolly" was written for astronauts Wally Schirra and Thomas P. Stafford and sung by crooner Jack Jones.

These are the custom lyrics:

Hello Wally, this is Jack Jones
Wally, it's so nice to know you're up where you belong.
All systems go, Wally, you're 4-0, Wally
Tom, all that's Navy Jazz for razzmatazz
You can't go wrong
While the earth's turning, the midnight oil was burning.
Gets you your requests from way back,
So, sit back with the wax, fellows, settle down and relax, fellows.
We'll see you down in Houston town again.[1]

WAKE-UP MUSIC BECOMES A NASA TRADITION

While music was beamed to the crews onboard Gemini 7, 9 and 12, it was done in batches and often during times of free time. The tradition of sending music on a regular basis as a wake-up call didn't start until Apollo 10. Since then, the tradition has become a way to not only wake up the astronauts, but to "promote a sense of camaraderie among the astronauts and ground support personnel." The selection of music is personalized to each crew and their mission, and is selected by CAPCOM, who often asked the crew's family and loved ones for suggestions.

APOLLO 11: WAKEUP NEWS

Rather than music to wake up to, the crew of Apollo 11 had wake-up calls that consisted of news and sports. NASA went back to sending music for Apollo 12.

FIRST SPACE SHUTTLE WAKE-UP CALL

For the first space shuttle mission, the very first wake-up music was "Blast-off Columbia," an original song written by Jerry W. Rucker, a NASA shuttle technician, and performed by Roy McCall.[2]

THE MOST PLAYED WAKE-UP SONG

- "What a Wonderful World" by Louis Armstrong – played 17 different times (it was played twice on the same mission, once each for two different astronauts.)[3]

WAKE-UP SONGS PLAYED 15 TIMES

- "Anchors Aweigh" is the U.S. Navy theme song
- "Off We Go into the Wild Blue Yonder" is the U.S. Air Force theme song

WAKE-UP SONGS PLAYED 8, 9, AND 10 TIMES

- "Beautiful Day" by U2 – played 10 times
- "Good Day Sunshine" by The Beatles – played 9 times
- "Marine Corps Hymn" – played 8 times

WAKE UP SONGS PLAYED 7 TIMES

- "Top of the World" by The Carpenters
- "I'll be Home for Christmas"
- "Rocket Man (I Think It's Going to Be A Long, Long Time)" by Elton John
- "2001, A Space Odyssey" movie theme song

WAKE UP SONGS PLAYED 5 AND 6 TIMES

- "Ride of the Valkyries" by Richard Wagner – 6 times
- "Star Wars Theme" by John Williams – 6 times

- "Homeward Bound" by Simon and Garfunkel – 5 times
- "Gonna Fly Now" (Theme From 'Rocky')" – 5 times
- "Fly Me to the Moon" by Frank Sinatra – 5 times
- "Should I Stay or Should I Go" by the Clash – 5 times
- "Here Comes the Sun" by The Beatles – 5 times

STAR WARS MUSIC & DARTH VADER'S VOICE

As you would expect, the music from the famous sci-fi movie, *Star Wars* has made its way to space several times, eight times in total. The *Star Wars* main theme has been played six times, the Cantina Band song was played once, and Darth Vader's Theme was also played once.

In 1988, the crew of STS-27 not only woke up to the *Star Wars* main theme, but Darth Vader's voice coming through the airwaves with a special wakeup message.

The crew of STS-72 got to hear two different *Star Wars* theme songs in 1996; the main *Star Wars* Theme and Darth Vader's theme.

1984 – STS-41-G – Star Wars Main Theme
1988 – STS-27 – Star Wars Theme and Darth Vader's Voice with a wakeup message
1993 – STS -51 – Star Wars Theme
1996 – STS-72 – Star Wars Theme and Darth Vader's Theme
1999 – STS-96 – Star Wars Theme
2007 – STS-120 – Star Wars Theme
2009 – STS-125 – Cantina Band

JIM HENSON AND THE MUPPETS' WAKE-UP CALL

Sally Ride, the first American woman in space, served as CAPCOM before her historic flight. She arranged several special and personalized wake-up calls with Jim Henson and the Muppets to be played to the two astronauts onboard space shuttle *Columbia* during STS-2. This was to be the first return trip to space for a spacecraft and only the second space shuttle trip.

The result was brilliant, and involved calls from the crew of the "USS Swinetrek" from *The Muppet Show*, with Captain Hogthrob, First

Mate Piggy and Dr. Strangepork to the crew of two, Commander Joe H. Engle and Pilot Richard Truly. The scripts had input from astronauts who knew the crew and there were plenty of inside jokes personalized to the crew. Listen for yourself at: https://youtu.be/Fa900RnL_aI

SPECIAL NOD TO *GROUNDHOG DAY*

In 2002, two crews onboard space shuttle *Endeavor*, the crews of STS-111 and STS-113, had to delay their flight back to Earth due to bad weather in Florida. Their last two days were spent performing and then repeating their deorbit activities. As a joke, NASA woke the crew up with Sonny and Cher's "I Got You Babe" on the extra days. This was a reference to the 1993 movie, *Groundhog Day*, where Bill Murray's character repeats the same day every day and wakes up to this song every morning.[4]

"GOOD MORNING, DISCOVERY!"

If you've seen the 1987 movie *Good Morning, Vietnam*, you can probably hear the phrase in Robin Williams's iconic style. Now imagine Robin Williams actually waking the crew of *Discovery* with "Good Morning, Discovery!" in that same style. That actually happened!

NASA arranged for Williams to deliver this special wake-up call because this wasn't just any wake-up call. This was the first wake-up call of the first space shuttle mission after the *Challenger* disaster in 1986, and a little extra something special was needed.

After Williams's intro, a modified version of the *Green Acres* theme played with personalized Shuttle-appropriate lyrics, followed by two more songs. These lyrics and these two songs are not included in NASA's historical records.[5]

Want to listen for yourself? You'll find a video on YouTube with Robin Williams' special wake-up call to the crew of *Discovery*.[6]

Astronaut Kathy Sullivan was assigned as CAPCOM for this special "Return to Flight" mission. She shares the full story on her podcast about how she worked with Robin Williams to deliver the memorable wake-up call. Listen to that here: https://www.kathysullivanexplores.com/podcast/waking-up-with-robin-williams

STAR TREK'S CAPTAIN JAMES T. KIRK WAKES THE ASTRONAUTS

On both STS-29 (March 1989) and STS-133 (March 2011), the *Discovery* shuttle astronauts got a special wake-up call with the *Star Trek* theme song and then comments from actor William Shatner, who played Captain Kirk in the original *Star Trek* television series.

As a final send-off for the space shuttle *Discovery*, a very special wake-up call was recorded for STS-133. On the morning of March 7, 2011, which marked the 39th mission and final mission for the space shuttle *Discovery*, William Shatner recorded this message that played over the *Star Trek* theme song:

> "Space: the final frontier.
> These have been the voyages of the space shuttle *Discovery*.
> Her thirty-year mission:
> To seek out new science, to build new outposts, to bring nations together on the final frontier.
> To boldly go and do what no spacecraft has done before."

To hear the wake-up call yourself, there's a video on YouTube with some NASA footage to go along with it.[7]

FOR *STAR TREK: THE NEXT GENERATION* FANS

The crew of *Atlantis* during mission STS-44 in November of 1991 were woken with a recording from actor Patrick Stewart, who at that time played Captain Jean-Luc Picard of the USS *Enterprise* on *Star Trek: The Next Generation*. While the theme song for *Star Trek: The Next Generation* played in the background, Patrick Stewart delivered this personalized message:

> "Space: the final frontier.
> This is the voyage of the Space Shuttle *Atlantis*.
> Its ten-day mission:
> To explore new methods of remote sensing and observation of the planet Earth...

To seek out new data on radiation in space, and a new understanding of the effects of microgravity on the human body...
To boldly go where two hundred and fifty-five men and women have gone before!"

"Hello Fred, Tom, Story, Jim, Tom, and especially Mario—this is Patrick Stewart, choosing not to outrank you as Captain Jean-Luc Picard, saying that we are confident of a productive and successful mission. **Make it so.**"

In case it wasn't obvious who the *Star Trek* fan among the crew was, it was astronaut Mario Runco.[8]

TOM SELLECK'S SPECIAL WAKE-UP CALL

Mission Specialist Linda Godwin, who also happens to be a Tom Selleck fan, had a special wake-up call during STS-37 in April 1991. Along with the *Magnum PI* TV show theme song playing, she had a message from Selleck that said, "Good morning, and a special wake-up to Linda. This is Tom Selleck and I hope you had a nice night's sleep, but it's time to get up and go to work."[9]

WAKE UP DADDY!

For the crew of STS-29, on the morning of March 18, 1989, they woke up to recordings of their kids saying "Get up, Dad, get out of bed and get to work," and "Hi daddy, this is your darling daughter telling you to wake up." Mission Control followed these messages up with Louis Armstrong's "What a Wonderful World." The crew sent their response back with Simon and Garfunkel's "Homeward Bound."[10]

COMMON LAST DAY IN SPACE WAKE-UP CALL SONG

On the last day before heading back to Earth, space shuttle crews would often wake up to Dean Martin's "Going Back to Houston." Although the crew would eventually make it back to Houston to debrief the mission, the shuttle itself never landed in Houston. The space shuttle would often land in Florida or California...but never Houston.[11]

ASTRONAUTS WAKING UP MISSION CONTROL

Occasionally, the space shuttle crews would send wake-up music to Mission Control.

The crew of Apollo 10 sent their own wake-up call to Houston in the form of "Come Fly with Me" on the morning of May 25th, 1969.[12]

During STS-29 in March 1989, the crew onboard *Discovery* woke up Mission Control with "Heigh-Ho, Heigh-Ho, It's Off To Work We Go" from the Disney movie *Snow White*.

In September 1993, during STS-51 the crew played "A Whole New World" for Mission Control and in response, Mission Control sent the "Star Wars Theme" to *Discovery*. During the same mission, the crew sent videotape views of Earth with the music "Theme for the Common Man" as a wake-up to Mission Control.

WAKE-UP CALLS ON MARS

Mission Control hasn't just sent music to astronauts in space, they've also sent music to the robotic explorers on Mars since 1997. The Mars Pathfinder and the Sojourner rover had the theme from the television show *Mad About You* called "The Final Frontier" played to them. Rover-appropriate songs like "Let the Good Times Roll" and "Love Me Like a Rock" have also been beamed to the Red Planet rovers.[13]

FINAL SHUTTLE WAKE-UP CALL

On the final morning of the last space shuttle mission on July 21, 2011, NASA woke up the crew of *Atlantis* with the song, "God Bless America," sung by Kate Smith, followed with some remarks to thank "all the men and women who put their heart and soul in the shuttle program all of these years."[14]

WAKE-UP CALLS ON THE ISS?

While the formal wake-up calls ended when the space shuttles were retired, the crew onboard the International Space Station do hear an occasionally wake-up call song. Italian astronaut, Samantha Cristoforetti tweeted about her personalized wake-up music, "La Cura" by Franco Battiato.[15]

THE RETURN OF NASA WAKE-UP CALLS

Now that NASA can launch its astronauts from American soil again, the wake-up call tradition seems to have resumed. The crew onboard Crew Dragon Space X Demo 2 flight woke to Black Sabbath's "Planet Caravan" the morning of May 31, 2020.[16]

In November 2020, before docking with the International Space Station, the four SpaceX Crew-1 astronauts on the Space X Crew Dragon were woken up by Phil Collins's "In the Air Tonight" after eight hours of sleeping.[17]

So, it looks like NASA's music wake-up call tradition is once again alive and well!

SPOTIFY NASA WAKE-UP CALL PLAYLIST

You can listen to most of these songs played for the space shuttle crews with a Spotify playlist. Find it here: https://spoti.fi/3P7tsky

ALL THE WAKE-UP CALLS

For the most complete list available of all of the documented wake-up songs in NASA's history, please see this list: https://history.nasa.gov/wakeup%20calls.pdf

Music Firsts in Space

FIRST SONG PERFORMED IN SPACE

Cosmonaut Pavlo Popvych was the fourth cosmonaut in space, eighth human in space and the first to sing a song in space in 1962. It was a Ukrainian song called "Watching the sky and thinking a thought."

Here's a snippet of the lyrics translated into English:

Watching the sky and thinking a thought:
Why am I not a falcon? Why am I not flying?

Why, Lord, have you not granted me wings?
I would the earth forsake and fly to the heavens.
Far beyond the clouds, further from earth away...[18]

This particular song was sung at the special request of the Soviet rocket engineer and spacecraft designer, Sergei Korolev. Korolev is considered the father of practical astronautics, oversaw the Soviet Space Program and was highly responsible for sending the first human in space.

PRANK & FIRST MUSICAL INSTRUMENTS IN SPACE

On December 16, 1965, Wally Schirra and Tom Stafford were onboard Gemini 6 when it successfully rendezvoused with Gemini 7. As a fun Christmas-themed prank, Wally radioed back to Houston that they could see an unidentified flying object in the sky flying a polar orbit from north to south. He went on to say that he could see "a command module and eight smaller modules in front. The pilot of the command module is wearing a red suit."

Wally then played a version of "Jingle Bells" on an eight-note Hohner "Little Lady" harmonica that was backed with miniature sleigh bells that they had snuck into the capsule for this very reason. Astronaut Jim Lovell on Gemini 7 confirmed the joke, and reported that they could see him too.[19] The space harmonica now lives in the Smithsonian National Air and Space Museum in Washington, D.C.[20]

FIRST AND ONLY DUET SUNG ON THE MOON

The last two people to visit the Moon were Apollo 17 astronauts Gene Cernan and Harrison Schmitt. During one of the four days they spent on the Moon collecting samples, Schmitt spontaneously and joyously started to sing his own version of "Strolling Through the Park One Day."

While bouncing on the surface of the Moon, Schmitt sings, "I was strolling on the Moon one day..." Cernan soon joins in and they both sing, "in the merry, merry month of December...May." They were on the Moon in December, but the original lyrics read May. Quickly the song falls apart after they both realize they don't know the rest of the words or how to adapt them to their situation.

Delightfully, the entire performance was caught on video and can be seen and heard on YouTube here: https://youtu.be/Zl_VdN6rfrQ

FIRST EVER EARTH/SPACE DUET

In 2011, to honor Yuri Gagarin's historic flight into space, American astronaut Cady Coleman and Jethro Tull's Ian Anderson played a flute duet fifty years after humans first made it to space.[21] Cady performed while onboard the International Space Station and Ian played while on tour in Perm, Russia. They played a portion of the song "Bourree," which was the same arrangement that Jethro Tull performed during their 1969 tour as the first men stepped on the Moon.[22]

FIRST ORBITAL DIDGERIDOO

As part of a science experiment, astronaut Don Petit became the first person to play a didgeridoo-type instrument in space. He fashioned the ISS space station vacuum cleaner hose into a didgeridoo and then showed us what happens to small spheres of water when he played his makeshift digeridoo next to them.[23]

FIRST BAGPIPER IN SPACE

Astronaut Kjell Lindgren is thought to have been the first to play the bagpipes in space during his ISS mission in 2015. Playing the bagpipes in space had been a two-year project for Kjell. He had reached out to a Scottish manufacturer two years before his mission to if they could make bagpipes that could be transported to and played in space. In November 2015, Kjell played "Amazing Grace," as a tribute to Victor Hurst, a research scientist and instructor who had died unexpectedly in October of that year.[24]

FIRST MUSIC VIDEO FILMED IN SPACE GOES VIRAL

With 50 million views and counting as of March 2022, Canadian astronaut Chris Hadfield's version of David Bowie's "Space Oddity"

Commander Chris Hadfield plays guitar in the Cupola Module on the ISS.
Photo courtesy of NASA.

set a Guinness World Record for being the first music video filmed in space when it was posted on May 12, 2013.

Commander Hadfield filmed the music video entirely in space and was the first to do so. The vocals and guitar were recorded while Commander Hadfield was on the ISS. The piano and other musical pieces were added by others on Earth. The Canadian Space Agency helped out with putting it together. Commander Hadfield got the appropriate permissions from David Bowie and even got a shoutout on Twitter in response after the video was posted on YouTube.[25] Bowie also remarked on Facebook that this was "possibly the most poignant version of the song ever created".[26] Watch it for yourself here: https://youtu.be/KaOC9danxNo

THE FIRST SAXOPHONE IN SPACE THAT THE WORLD NEVER HEARD

If you don't count the harmonica and sleigh bells smuggled onboard the Gemini VI, the first NASA-approved musical instrument was

Ron McNair playing the first saxophone in space in 1984. Source: NASA, courtesy AIP Emilio Segrè Visual Archives, Ronald E. Mickens Collection.

brought onboard by astronaut Ron McNair in 1984. He brought his saxophone on the shuttle and he did play it. But his performance never made the news. McNair even made a tape of him playing a medley of three songs while in space (one of those is thought to be the song "America"), but somehow the tape was recorded over before it could be played. Though the world did not get to hear the first saxophone in space,[27] there is a photo of Ron with his saxophone on the space shuttle *Challenger* in 1984.[28]

THE PLANNED SPACE MUSICAL FIRST THAT NEVER HAPPENED

For his next trip, Ron McNair brought his saxophone again, but this time he was going to play a special solo that had been composed by Jean Michel Jarr for his upcoming album *Rendez-Vous*. This would have been the first piece of music ever composed for and debuted in space. McNair's solo was going to be broadcast live to Earth at a Jean Michel Jarr concert in Houston while in space.

Sadly, this special musical first never happened. McNair was one of the seven crew members who died during the 1986 *Challenger* disaster. After the disaster, saxophonist Kirk Whalun recorded McNair's piece. It's included as the last track on Jean Michel Jarr's Rendez-Vous. The track is called, "The Last Rendez-Vous (Ron's Piece)"[29] and includes a special dedication from Jarr in the linear notes, "Ron was so excited about the piece that he rehearsed it continuously until the last moment. May the memory of my friend the astronaut and the artist Ron McNair live on through this piece."[30]

FIRST MUSIC FROM MARS

The first song to be beamed to Earth from Mars was a song by Black Eyed Peas' Will.i.am, "Reach for the Stars" and sent by the Curiosity Rover. This became the first song to be broadcast to Earth from another planet, and it had to travel 300 million miles to get here.

NOTES

1. Colin Fries, "Chronology of Wakeup Calls," NASA History Division (NASA, March 3, 2015), https://web.archive.org/web/20210307004710/https://history.nasa.gov/wakeup%20calls.pdf.

2. Fries, "Chronology of Wakeup Calls."

3. John Matson, "A Little Flight Music: NASA Contest for Wake-Up Songs Prompts Astronauts to Recall Tuneful Highlights," Scientific American, August 27, 2010, https://www.scientificamerican.com/article/nasa-shuttle-music/.

4. Matt Blitz, "How the NASA Wake-Up Call Went From an Inside Joke to a Beloved Tradition," Popular Mechanics, February 15, 2018, https://www.popularmechanics.com/space/a26229/nasa-wake-up-call/.

5. Chris Higgins, "11 Eye-Opening NASA Wakeup Calls," Mental Floss, July 11, 2012, https://www.mentalfloss.com/article/31156/11-eye-opening-nasa-wakeup-calls.

6. Video with the audio of Robin Williams' wake-up call: https://youtu.be/S7WJtQYU8i4

7. Listen to the special wake-up call audio and watch Space Shuttle Discovery video footage here: https://www.youtube.com/watch?v=ZghBLz7S3D4

8. Higgins, "11 Eye-Opening NASA Wakeup Calls."

9. Fries, "Chronology of Wakeup Calls."

10. Fries, "Chronology of Wakeup Calls."

11. Mike Wall, "Lost Space Shuttle Tradition? Astronaut Wake-Up Songs May Retire With Fleet," Space.com, July 20, 2011, https://www.space.com/12360-astronaut-wakeup-songs-space-shuttle-retirement.html.

12. Fries, "Chronology of Wakeup Calls."

13. Brian Dunbar, "Music to Wake Up By," ed. Jim Wilson, NASA (NASA, November 30, 2007), https://www.nasa.gov/vision/space/features/wakeup_calls.html.

14. Listen for yourself: "STS-135 Final Wakeup Call," *STS-135 Final Wakeup Call* (NASA, July 21, 2011), http://ia600203.us.archive.org/8/items/STS-135/07-21-11_STS-135_FD14_Crew_Wakeup.wav.

15. Samantha Cristoforetti (@AstroSamantha), "This morning Franco's music woke me up #Battiato … overcoming "the gravitational currents, space and light ":-) @RaiNews," Twitter, April 17, 2015, https://twitter.com/astrosamantha/status/588968966875394049.

16. Anna Heiney, "NASA's SpaceX Demo-2: Watch Arrival of Astronauts Behnken and Hurley to Space Station," NASA (NASA, May 31, 2020), https://blogs.nasa.gov/commercialcrew/2020/05/31/nasas-spacex-demo-2-watch-arrival-of-astronauts-behnken-and-hurley-to-space-station/.

17. Mark Garcia, "NASA's SpaceX Crew-1 Mission," NASA (NASA, May 4, 2021), https://blogs.nasa.gov/crew-1/.

18. Eugene Bouquet and Alexander Petrenko, *I Look at the Sky and Think*, trans. by Jbuket (Zhytomyr: Yevenok OO [ed.], 2017, 50, https://uk.wikipedia.org/w/index.php?title=%D0%A4%D0%B0%D0%B9%D0%BB:Translation_book_of_%22Watching_the_Sky_and_Thinking_a_Thought%22.pdf&page=50.

19. Hear the audio clip here: *The Song from Outer Space*, YouTube (BuzzLab, 2011), https://youtu.be/HqfIEQKnkJU.

20. Owen Edwards, "The Day Two Astronauts Said They Saw a U.F.O. Wearing a Red Suit," Smithsonian.com (Smithsonian Institution, December 1, 2005), https://www.smithsonianmag.com/history/day-two-astronauts-said-they-saw-ufo-santa-suit-109444898/.

21. Watch their duet here: *Space Flute Duet*, YouTube (NASA, 2013), https://youtu.be/z4JkLutikF0.

22. Brian Dunbar, "NASA Astronaut Cady Coleman, Jethro Tull's Ian Anderson Perform First Space-Earth Flute Duet," NASA (NASA, last modified August 7, 2017), https://www.nasa.gov/home/hqnews/2011/apr/HQ_11-108_Coleman_space_duet.html.

23. See the first orbital didgeridoo performance: "Science off the Sphere: Space Soundwaves II- Electric Didgeridoo," YouTube (Physics Central, May 30, 2012), https://youtu.be/Uz_vvdCVPqA.

24. Justin Worland, "Astronaut Plays Bagpipes on the International Space Station," Time (Time, November 8, 2015), https://time.com/4104158/international-space-station-bagpipe/.

25. Chris Hadfield, "First Music Video Filmed in Space," Guinness World Records, May 13, 2013, https://www.guinnessworldrecords.com/world-records/first-music-video-filmed-in-space.

26. Andrew Griffin, "When Chris Hadfield's Poignant Space Oddity Got Taken down, David Bowie Came to the Rescue," The Independent (Independent Digital News and Media, January 11, 2016), https://www.independent.co.uk/arts-entertainment/music/david-bowie-how-chris-hadfield-space-oddity-cover-orbit-was-helped-real-starman-a6805586.html.

27. Kurt Heisig, "Sax in Space ," Kurt Heisig Music, 1986, https://www.kurtheisigmusic.com/sax-in-space/.

28. See the photo of Ron here: "Ron McNair Plays Sax in Space, 1984," MIT Black History, accessed May 31, 2021, https://www.blackhistory.mit.edu/archive/ron-mcnair-plays-sax-space-1984.

29. Rebecca J. Rosen, "A Brief History of Musical Firsts in Space," The Atlantic (Atlantic Media Company, December 27, 2012), https://www.theatlantic.com/technology/archive/2012/12/a-brief-history-of-musical-firsts-in-space/266637/.

30. Listen to "Last Rendez-Vous (Ron's Piece)" here: *Jean Michel Jarre - Last Rendez-Vous (Ron's Piece) - "Challenger"*, YouTube (DeltaFox1970, 2008), https://www.youtube.com/watch?v=jtGG1WLP1pk.

SPACE & THE OLYMPICS

OLYMPIC TORCH IN SPACE

The Olympic torch—excluding the flame for safety reasons—has been taken into space by astronauts and cosmonauts in 1996, 2000 and 2013, and has flown over every nation competing at the Olympic Games.[1]

THE FIRST OLYMPIC TORCH IN SPACE

For the 1996 Summer Olympics in Atlanta, Georgia, the unlit torch was taken into space onboard the Space Shuttle *Columbia* as part of STS-78. It spent almost 17 days in space before making its way back to Earth to continue the Olympic torch relay to Atlanta.

THE SECOND OLYMPIC TORCH IN SPACE & FIRST ON THE ISS

The Space Shuttle *Atlantis* carried the unlit torch into space and to the International Space Station during STS-101 for the 2000 Summer Olympics in Sydney, Australia. While this wasn't the first time the Olympic torch made it into space, it was the first time that the torch made it to the ISS and the first time the relay made its way underwater. A special flare-like torch that burned at 3,362 °F (2,000°C) was taken underwater on a dive down to the Great Barrier Reef.

FIRST OLYMPIC TORCH RELAY ON A SPACEWALK

In preparation for the Sochi Olympics in Russia, the Olympic torch made its way to the International Space Station in November 2013.[2] While in space, the Olympic torch went on its first-ever spacewalk, where it was exposed to the vacuum of space and handed off from cosmonaut Sergey Ryazanckiy to cosmonaut Oleg Kotov.[3]

COSMONAUT RUNS RELAY ON SPACE TREADMILL

After the Olympic torch had its time outside the ISS, it was brought

Russian cosmonaut Fyodor Yurchikhin welcomes cosmonaut Mikhail Tyurin as he arrives onboard the ISS with the Olympic torch. Photo courtesy of NASA.[4]

back inside and cosmonaut Oleg Kotov ran with it on the space station treadmill to simulate a marathon.

ISS CREW OLYMPIC TORCH RELAY
The rest of the crew onboard the ISS got involved and took part in a special weightless space relay with each crew member taking turns floating with the torch down portions of the space station and handing it off to the next crew member for the entire length of the International Space Station.[5]

SPECIAL OLYMPIC TORCH MISSION PATCH
Cosmonauts Oleg Kotov and Sergey Ryanzanskiy wore special Olympic patches on their spacesuits as another way to commemorate the historic spacewalk with the Olympic torch.[6]

COSMONAUTS LAUNCH THE SOCHI WINTER OLYMPICS

The 2014 Winter Olympic Games officially opened in Sochi, Russia, when the torch that was flown into space was used to light the Olympic Cauldron. Noteworthy Earth-bound cosmonauts were among the 14,000 torch-bearers for the Sochi Games that carried the flame on Earth. Two of the torch-bearers were cosmonauts Mikhail Kornienko and Valentina Tereshkova. They spent a year together in space. Tereshkova was the first woman in space.[7]

2012 OLYMPIC PIN SENT TO SPACE 12 YEARS EARLIER

NASA sent 1,000 Olympic pins into space 12 years ahead of the 2012 Olympic Games. When these pins were created and flown into space, it wasn't yet known which city would host those Games. Houston, New York, San Francisco and Washington, D.C.-Baltimore were all bidding to represent the U.S. Optimistically, NASA had lapel pins created in the shape of the space shuttle with a Texas flag torch logo with "Houston, 2012" inscribed below.

In May 2000, Space Shuttle *Atlantis* launched with 1,000 of these pins onboard and returned with these space-flown Houston 2012 Olympic pins ready for distribution to the Houston 2012 Foundation members, supporters and NASA employees.

However, Houston did not win the competition. New York represented the U.S. Eventually, the International Olympic Committee voted in 2005.[8] London won the bid and became the host city for the 2012 Olympics.

NOTES

1. Robert Z. Pearlman, "Spacewalking Cosmonauts 'Run' Historic Olympic Torch Relay in Space," Space.com, November 9, 2013, https://www.space.com/23537-spacewalking-cosmonauts-run-historic-olympic-torch-relay-in-space.html.

2. Brian Dunbar, "Olympic Torch Completes Longest Relay in History," ed. Jerry Wright, NASA (NASA, August 7, 2017), https://www.nasa.gov/content/olympic-torch-completes-longest-relay-in-history.

3. See the video here: "An Olympic Moment in Space," YouTube (NASA, November 9, 2013), https://youtu.be/4MrnqEf3i-U.

4. Brian Dunbar, "New Station Crew Arrives with Olympic Torch," ed. Jerry Wright, NASA (NASA, last modified August 7, 2017, https://www.nasa.gov/content/new-station-crew-arrives-with-olympic-torch.

5. See the video here: *Sochi 2014 Olympic Torch on International Space Station*, YouTube (collectSpace, 2014), https://youtu.be/7gQRhi1dsCI.

6. "Cosmonauts Wore Special Space Patch for Olympic Torch Spacewalk," collectSPACE.com, November 10, 2013, http://www.collectspace.com/news/news-111013a.html.

7. "Sochi Winter Olympics Launch with Space-Flown Torch, Cosmonaut Flag-Bearers," collectSPACE.com, February 7, 2014, http://www.collectspace.com/news/news-020714a-olympics-opening-ceremony-space-torch.html.

8. "How NASA Launched the 2012 Olympics 12 Years Ago: a Pin Payload's Story," collectSPACE.com, January 27, 2012, http://www.collectspace.com/news/news-072712a.html.

LOST OBJECTS IN SPACE

A Few Objects Lost Over the Years

"OOPS, THERE GOES YOUR GLOVE!"

The very first item lost by an astronaut was a glove. Ed White lost it during the first American spacewalk in 1965. While White was outside Gemini 4, his crewmate James McDivitt was taking pictures from inside the spacecraft. The hatch was open and White's optional outer comfort glove floated out of the hatch and over his right shoulder on a trajectory all its own. "Oops, there goes your glove," said McDivitt as he continued to take pictures as it floated away. It burned up[1] about a month later as it re-entered the Earth's atmosphere.[2]

HOUSTON, HAVE YOU SEEN MY CAMERA?

In June 2007, American astronaut Sunita Williams lost her camera while she was working on the International Space Station during a spacewalk. The bracket the camera was attached to came undone and it drifted away. This unfortunate event was caught on camera and can be viewed on YouTube at https://youtu.be/ZYRHloqW_fw

During one of the earliest spacewalks in August 1966, astronaut Mike Collins lost his grip on a Hasselblad super-wide camera and Sweden got its first satellite.[3]

"GUYS? I THINK MY SPATULA ESCAPED"

Astronaut and meteorologist Piers Sellers lost his 14-inch spatula about halfway into a 7-hour, 11-minute-long spacewalk in 2006. The orbiting spatula became known as the "spat sat" and was tracked by NORAD (North American Aerospace Defense Command). Four months later the spatula re-entered the atmosphere, became a shooting star and burned up.[4]

LOST WRIST MIRROR

While stepping out of the International Space Station to perform a spacewalk, US Commander Chris Cassidy lost his left wrist mirror in June 2020. These mirrors allow astronauts to see switches and labeling on the front of the suit that are normally out of view. But Cassidy was able to use his right wrist mirror for the rest of the spacewalk.

LOST NEEDLE-NOSE PLIERS

A set of needle-nose pliers were seen floating away at the end of a seven-hour spacewalk where astronaut and emergency room physician Scott Parazynski successfully repaired a damaged solar array.[5]

THE ISS TOOL BAG SEEN FROM EARTH

While repairing a part of the ISS in November 2008, US astronaut Heide Stefanyshyn-Piper discovered a grease gun had leaked. She was working to clean it up when her tool bag quickly drifted away out of reach.

The bag was about the size of a small suitcase and weighed 30 lbs. (13.6 kg). It contained grease guns, a scraper tool, and other tools needed to fix a rotary joint. This bag was worth about $100,000 and was large enough for amateur astronomers to spot it from Earth. The bag became a shooting star the following August when it re-entered the Earth's atmosphere above the Pacific or Indian Ocean.[6]

LOST AND FOUND WEDDING RING ON TRIP TO THE MOON

Two days into an 11-day trip to the Moon in 1972, American astronaut Ken Mattingly misplaced his wedding ring. It "just floated away" and was nowhere to be found inside the command module. It wasn't until day nine when they were on their way home, that it finally come out from hiding.

Mattingly and his spacewalk partner Charlie Duke were outside the spacecraft performing an experiment. While Mattingly was busy with the experiment, Duke had turned around to head back in. The hatch was open and he saw something glistening in the sun as it floated out of the hatch. Duke reached out to grab the ring, but missed. The ring continued to float away and headed straight towards Mattingly. Amazingly, the ring bounced off the back of his helmet and floated right into Duke's hand![7]

LOST TANK OF AMMONIA

NASA gave the astronauts permission to release an unneeded 1,400-pound (635-kg) tank of ammonia. Originally, the tank was part of the space station's cooling system, but when it was upgraded, the tank was no longer needed and was just taking up space. Due to cargo room restrictions, the mission manager decided that it should be released into space instead of bringing it back to Earth. The tank was carefully tracked and it eventually burned up over the South Pacific Ocean as it re-entered the Earth's atmosphere over a year later.[8]

HAVE YOU SEEN THAT FOURTH PANEL?

In March 2017, two very experienced astronauts had the task of placing four large protective panels over a docking port. After placing three of the four panels, they turned to retrieve the final panel and discovered it wasn't where it should have been. It had become unsecured and was drifting below the space station on its way back to Earth.[9]

COSMONAUT ALMOST LOST IN SPACE

On his first spacewalk, Russian cosmonaut Oleg Skripochka was working on the Russian service module on the ISS when he became untethered and started to drift away. The only thing that saved him from being the first person lost in space was that he hit an antenna. This impact had enough force to send him floating back close enough to the station for him to grab onto a handrail.[10]

"WANTED POSTERS" FOR LOST OBJECTS ON THE ISS

Weightlessness makes it really easy for things to just wander off. Items drifting off and getting lost happens regularly. Ground control has been known to email the crew WANTED posters for some of the lost items. As of 2022, eight years is the record for the longest time it took a missing item to reappear.[11]

Space Debris

FLOATING GRAVEYARD OF SPACE DEBRIS

Every orbital launch creates space debris. Some pieces burn up when they drop out of orbit and re-enter Earth's atmosphere. Some don't burn up upon re-entry, but land somewhere on Earth—usually in the ocean. Others stay in orbit for years and some might stay in orbit forever. It's been called a floating graveyard of space junk.

Most space debris is large enough to be tracked. Current estimates project these objects orbiting Earth: 16,300 objects larger than 3.9 inches (10 cm), about the size of a bagel; 60,000 objects larger than 1.9 inches (5 cm), or the size of a kiwi fruit; 200,000,000 objects larger than 0.04 inches (1 mm), or the tip of a pencil; and 1,000,000,000 objects larger than 0.004 inches (0.1 mm), or the size of fine glitter.

TRACKING HUMAN-MADE DEBRIS

Tracking space debris is serious business, and currently the U.S. Air Force and U.S. Space Force tracks tens of thousands of human-made objects that are orbiting Earth.[12]

SEE THE SPACE DEBRIS AND SATELLITES FOR YOURSELF

James Yoder, a computer programmer, created a website called "Stuff in Space" that visually tracks the paths of hundreds of thousands of objects currently orbiting Earth in real-time.

The Stuff in Space works best on Safari and Firefox browsers and can be accessed at https://bit.ly/stuff-in-space. Chrome doesn't load properly on Macs and doesn't show the full debris. Load the site and you'll see a spinning Earth surrounded with different colored dots. The red dots represent satellites, the gray dots represent debris and the blue dots represent discarded rocket bodies.[13] Hovering over a dot will show you its name. Clicking on a dot will bring up the object and tell you if it's debris, a rocket body, or a payload, which in this case means satellite. There's also a search function that allows you to search for specific objects or for groups. For fun, you can type in Starlink and see all of the Starlink satellites.

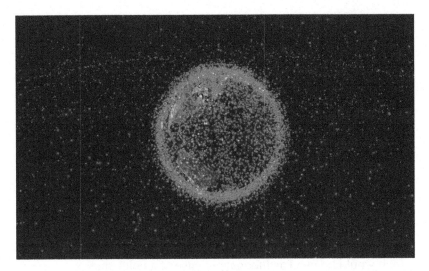

Tracked objects in Earth's orbit as seen on the "Stuff in Space" website.[14]

LARGEST PIECES OF SPACE DEBRIS

The largest pieces of debris to fall back to Earth include the retired space station Skylab in 1979, Skylab's rocket stage in 1975 and the Salyut 7 in 1991. The Space Shuttle *Columbia* that broke up and disintegrated during re-entry and killed everyone onboard could also be included as one of the larger pieces of space debris, especially since it became uncontrolled on its way back down to Earth.[15]

TOP 50 MOST DANGEROUS PIECES OF SPACE JUNK

In October 2020, 11 teams from 13 countries and organizations— including teams from Russia, the US, China, Japan and Europe—got together and came up with a list of what they thought were the most dangerous pieces of space debris currently orbiting Earth.

The first 20 objects on the list are all large rocket boosters launched by Russia and the Soviet Union between 1987 and 2007. Each of these boosters weighs 9.9 tons (9,000 kg). To put this into perspective, that's heavier than the weight of two full-grown male hippopotamuses.[16]

Other dangerous items on the list include several satellites, including the European Space Agency's defunct ENVISAT satellite weighing 17,200 lbs. (7,800 kg) and launched in 2002. Also on the list are Japan's ADEOS I and II satellites launched in 1996 and 2002.[17]

ACCIDENTAL DEBRIS COLLISION

As of June 2022, only one major space collision has occurred. In February 2009, a working US Iridium satellite accidently collided with an old deactivated Russian Cosmos satellite. They collided at the speed of 26,000 mph or (42,000 kph) at an altitude of 490 miles (789 km). Experts have estimated that the collision created over 2,000 fragments 4 inches (10 cm) or larger.[18]

A small piece of the destroyed Cosmos satellite got close enough to the International Space Station in 2012 that the six astronauts and cosmonauts onboard were instructed to stay in the two docked Soyuz, which would be used as lifeboats in case of a collision.[19]

More recently in November 2021, Russia destroyed one of their own dead satellites, Kosmos 1408. This created a massive debris cloud with more than 1,500 pieces of trackable debris and hundreds of thousands of untrackable debris. The ISS was traveling close enough to it, that the seven astronauts and cosmonauts onboard the ISS had to shelter inside the docked Crew Dragon and Soyuz spacecrafts for a short time.[20]

ANTI-SATELLITE DEBRIS

While anti-satellite space weapons have never been used in an act of war, there have been times where a few nations have demonstrated the power they have to destroy or disable satellites. An anti-satellite demonstration in 2007 by the Chinese created a cloud of debris that will be in orbit for decades. Several times a year, the International Space Station must maneuver out of the way of this debris cloud, which costs millions of dollars in fuel each time.[21]

DEAD SATELLITES

As of January 2021, there were 3,170 dead satellites that are now space junk.[22]

THE DAM – HOW THE ISS AVOIDS SPACE DEBRIS

NASA keeps a close eye on the bigger pieces of space debris. If something looks like it might get too close to the International Space Station, they will instruct the ISS to perform what's called a DAM. DAM stands for Debris Avoidance Maneuver. The ISS makes the necessary orbit adjustments by using the Russian Service Module rocket engines.[23]

HOW LONG DOES SPACE JUNK STAY IN ORBIT?

This depends on how high the space debris is. The higher the altitude, the longer it will remain in Earth's orbit. Debris orbiting below 373 miles (600 km) will normally re-enter Earth's atmosphere and burn up within several years. At altitudes of 497 miles (800 km), it's estimated to take hundreds of years. Space debris orbiting above 621 miles (1,000 km) will continue to orbit the Earth for a thousand years or more.[24]

For perspective, the International Space Station is orbiting the Earth at an average altitude of 254 miles (408 km).

HOW TO SEE THE SPACE DEBRIS FROM EARTH

If you know what to look for, you can see the larger space debris from Earth. Find a dark place, far from the light pollution caused by city lights and look up into the sky about an hour after sunset. Look for small white points of light moving slowly across the sky. They will not be blinking like airplanes do.

NOTES

1.   Clara Moskowitz, "Lost in Space: 8 Weird Pieces of Space Junk," Wired (Conde Nast, July 30, 2018), https://www.wired.com/2009/02/spacestuff/.

2.   Robert Z. Pearlman, "Five Floating Facts for the 50th Anniversary of the 1st American Spacewalk," Space.com, June 3, 2015, https://www.space.com/29556-first-american-spacewalk-five-facts.html.

3.   "The Hasselblad Camera," HasselbladFoundation.org, accessed April 22, 2022, https://www.hasselbladfoundation.org/wp/history/the-hasselblad-camera/.

4. *What Happens When an Astronaut Drops Something in Space?* | *Short Film Showcase*, YouTube (National Geographic, 2017), https://www.youtube.com/watch?v=rbA9q7JdzZs.

5. John Schwartz, "Space Station Is Repaired in Spacewalk," The New York Times, November 4, 2007, https://www.nytimes.com/2007/11/04/science/space/04shuttle.html.

6. "RIP ISS Tool Bag," Science (American Association for the Advancement of Science, August 14, 2009), https://science.sciencemag.org/content/325/5942/797.3.

7. Zoe Mendelson, "That Time an Astronaut Lost His Wedding Ring in Space," Wired (Conde Nast, June 3, 2017), https://www.wired.com/2016/06/time-astronaut-lost-wedding-ring-space/.

8. Moskowitz, "Lost in Space."

9. Tim Peake, *Ask an Astronaut: My Guide to Life in Space* (Little Brown and Company, 2017), 167.

10. Scott Kelly, *Endurance: A Year in Space, A Lifetime of Discovery* (New York: Alfred A. Knopf, 2017), 276.

11. Kelly, *Endurance*, 73.

12. Terry Virts, *How to Astronaut: An Insider's Guide to Leaving Planet Earth* (New York, Workman Publishing, 2020), 100.

13. Carl Franzen, "See All The Satellites And Space Junk Circling Earth In Real-Time," Popular Science, July 9, 2015, https://www.popsci.com/now-you-can-see-all-space-junk-floating-around-earth-real-time/.

14. "Stuff in Space," Stuff in Space, accessed March 31, 2022, https://web.archive.org/web/20220331191856/http://stuffin.space/

15. Allen Kim, "One of the Largest Uncontrolled Pieces of Space Debris Fell down to Earth Today," CNN (Cable News Network, May 11, 2020), https://www.cnn.com/2020/05/11/us/china-rocket-scn-trnd/index.html.

16. Kassandra Mason, "Hippopotamus Amphibius (Hippopotamus)," Animal Diversity Web, accessed May 31, 2021, https://animaldiversity.org/site/accounts/information/Hippopotamus_amphibius.html.

17. Jonathan O'Callaghan, "These Are The 50 Most Dangerous Objects Orbiting Earth Right Now," Forbes (Forbes Magazine, September 10, 2020), https://www.forbes.com/sites/jonathanocallaghan/2020/09/10/experts-reveal-the-50-most-dangerous-pieces-of-space-junk-orbiting-earth-right-now/?sh=65cf99aa7c21.

18. "International Space Station Again Dodges Debris," *Orbital Debris Quarterly News* 15, no. 3 (July 2011), https://web.archive.org/web/20111020092342/http://orbitaldebris.jsc.nasa.gov/newsletter/pdfs/ODQNv15i3.pdf.

19. *Orbital Debris Safely Passes International Space Station*, YouTube (NASA, 2012), https://youtu.be/Kw5zkf2ZfvA.

20. Eric Burger, "Russia aym have just shot down its own satellite, creating a huge debris cloud," ARSTechnica, accessed November 15, 2021, https://arstechnica.com/science/2021/11/debris-from-a-satellite-shot-down-by-the-russians-appears-to-threaten-the-iss/

21. Virts, *How to Astronaut*, 100-101.

22. O'Callaghan, "50 Most Dangerous Objects Orbiting Earth."

23. Virts, *How to Astronaut*, 101-102.

24. "FAQ," ARES Orbital Debris Program Office (NASA), accessed May 31, 2021, https://orbitaldebris.jsc.nasa.gov/faq/#.

WHAT ASTRONAUTS MISS WHILE IN SPACE

Space can be a lonely place full of uncomfortable experiences. Here's what astronauts have said they miss after being away from Earth for a bit.

SMELLS OF EARTH

The smell of space has been described as burnt metal or rubber. Astronauts find themselves missing the smells of Earth. While onboard the Russian space station Mir, resupply vehicles would include letters from women who would put drops of French perfume on them. These letters were treasured by the male crew onboard.[1]

SOUNDS OF EARTH

One of the most popular and uplifting things astronauts onboard the International Space Station enjoy listening to is a "Sounds of Earth" MP3 file that was sent up by one of their psychologists. The MP3 file includes recordings of rain, wind through the trees, waves, birdcalls, a crowded café, and even the buzz of mosquitos.[2]

CRUNCHY FOOD

Many astronauts in space miss munching on crunchy food. Crunchy food often can break apart into tiny pieces and becomes a hazard in space. This means crunchy and crumbly food is banned on the ISS. Space food is also usually rehydrated or canned, which also means food is cooked and is soft. Some of the foods astronauts miss the most are chips, crunchy crusty bread and fresh crunchy fruits and vegetables like apples, carrots, and celery.

FRESH FRUITS & VEGETABLES

The only fresh fruits and vegetables that astronauts eat while in space is what is brought up in resupply vehicles. In space, things tend to go bad more quickly than on Earth, so they have to be eaten within the first few days. The small refrigerator onboard is for experiments, not food. So fresh fruits and vegetables are rare and something many astronauts look forward to eating again once back on Earth.

THEY HAVE WALKING DREAMS

Many of us dream of being weightless and flying through the air like Superman. Astronauts who live in weightlessness for an extended period of time have found themselves dreaming of walking.

Cosmonaut Aleksandr Laveykin, who spent a total of 174 days, 3 hours and 25 minutes in space has said, "Only in space do you understand what incredible happiness it is just to walk. To walk on Earth." [3]

NOTES

1.   Mary Roach, *Packing for Mars: The Curious Science of Life in the Void* (New York, NY: WW Norton, 2011), 58-59.

2.   Scott Kelly, *Endurance: A Year in Space, A Lifetime of Discovery* (New York: Alfred A. Knopf, 2017), 73.

3.   Roach, *Packing for Mars*, 58.

COMING BACK TO EARTH

THE JOURNEY HOME
After undocking from the International Space Station, it takes about 3.5 hours and sometimes up to six hours to land back on Earth.

DANGEROUS JOURNEY
The trip back home isn't easy or safe. Both astronauts and cosmonauts have died on the return trip. One of the dangers includes how they enter the Earth's atmosphere. If they come in too steep, they fall too fast and can be killed by the intense amount of heat or the excessive weight of deceleration. If they come in too shallow, the spacecraft will bounce off Earth's atmosphere, much like what happens when you throw a rock and skip it across a still lake.[1]

SOYUZ STORAGE SPACE
Most of the storage space in the Soyuz is for emergency landing items that the crews hope to never use: radio, compass, machete, and cold-weather survival gear in case they land off-course and have to wait for search and rescue teams.[2]

For a while a small, lightweight pistol was included in the emergency survival kits after cosmonauts Alexei Leonov and Pavel Belyayev landed off-course in Siberia. They spent a very cold night in their capsule waiting for search and rescue while wolves circled outside.[3]

RE-ENTRY PRESSURE SUITS ARE REQUIRED
All astronauts and cosmonauts wear the same suits they wore when they launched into space, their pressure suits. These are different from EVA spacesuits, but are very important and could save their lives in a number of different accidents. When they re-enter Earth's atmosphere, temperatures reach around 3000°F (1,650°C), and anywhere between 4 to 10 g's (4 to 10 times the amount of gravity) press against them as they decelerate.[4]

GOING OVER NIAGARA FALLS IN A BARREL, WHILE ON FIRE

Coming back to Earth is an intensely bumpy ride for the crew onboard capsules like the Soyuz. Even after the chute opens, the capsule often hits the ground around 15 mph (24 kph), bounces, and rolls a bit.[5] Italian astronaut Samantha Cristoforetti described it as the "sensation of going over Niagara Falls in a barrel, while on fire." Others have compared it to a train accident followed by a car accident followed by falling off your bike.[6]

DON'T BITE YOUR TONGUE

A warning is given to the crews right before the moment of impact— do not open their mouths to prevent them from accidently biting their tongues.

LYING DOWN DURING RE-ENTRY

There is no returning your seat to an upright position when you're returning to Earth. To keep the blood from pooling in their legs and feet when they are re-introduced to the full weight of Earth's gravity, astronauts and cosmonauts always lie down during re-entry.[7]

PRE-LANDING FLUID LOADING

Body fluids shift while in space, and the body doesn't need as much fluid. Astronauts end up having to pee a lot when they first get to space. This reduces the overall amount of fluid in their body. This isn't a problem in space, but can cause fainting and dehydration when they return to Earth. To prevent this, returning astronauts have a fluid-loading system. Starting 90 minutes before they land, astronauts drink a series of drinks every 15 minutes. They can drink anything from water with salt tablets, Powerade, chicken broth or any kind of salty water.[8]

RUSSIANS WEAR ANTIGRAVITY SUITS

Most Soyuz crews wear these compression shorts and gaiters underneath their Sokol spacesuits. They're made of elasticated fabric

The view inside the Soyuz just after Expedition 48 landed. Photo courtesy of NASA/Bill Ingalls.[9]

and can be tightened with laces. The suits reduce the pooling of blood in their lower bodies and maintains arterial pressure.[10]

CARRIED TO LOUNGE CHAIRS

After cosmonauts and astronauts return to Earth in the Russian Soyuz spacecraft, the search and rescue teams pull them out and carry them to three lounge chairs that have been set in front of the capsule. They are given a quick medical checkup, rest for about 30 minutes, and call home on the satellite phone.

FAINTING ASTRONAUTS

In space, astronauts have 10% to 15% less blood than they do on Earth. When they return to Earth, a combination of low blood volume, arteries and veins that haven't had to work as hard to transport blood through the body, and reintroducing the full weight of gravity can cause blood to pool in their legs and feet. This is called orthostatic

NASA Astronaut Christina Koch being carried to the medical tent shortly after landing onboard Expedition 61 Soyuz landing. Photo courtesy of NASA.

hypotension and can cause astronauts to feel lightheaded. Some astronauts have also fainted due to this soon after they return home.[11] There's a reason they rest in lounge chairs for a while before talking to the media.

EARTH SICKNESS

Space sickness happens in space, but when they return to Earth astronauts can also experience what's known as earth sickness or landing vertigo. Astronauts will often take anti-sickness medication to help.[12]

POST-LANDING CEREMONY

For crews that land in the Russian Soyuz spacecraft, after they've had time to rest, call home, and have a more in-depth medical evaluation, they are taken to the Dzez airport by helicopter. There is a post-landing ceremony where the crews are dressed in ceremonial Russian caps and hats and given matryoshka dolls decorated with their image along with the traditional bread and salt. Crews are then escorted onto the planes that will take them home.[13]

FLIGHT HOME ON GULFSTREAM III OR IV

About five hours after they land, ESA and NASA astronauts fly home on one of NASA's Gulfstream business jets, the Gulfstream III or Gulfstream IV. Onboard, the astronauts are monitored and kept comfortable. They are often tired, so there are comfortable beds on board and medical personnel that make sure they have everything they need. For a little taste of home, the crewmembers' families often send their favorite food and drinks.

The medical personnel also collect body fluids from the astronauts in the name of science.[14] It is important that samples are extracted soon after they return before the astronauts bodies can readjust to gravity, air and sunlight. It's also important to make sure they are healthy.[15]

NASA's modified Gulfstream III business jet. Photo courtesy of NASA.

Readjusting & Aftereffects

It can take some time for astronauts to adjust to coming back to Earth. They often are very tired and sleep a lot. Their heartbeat can be elevated—even while at rest. Different parts of their body hurt from just sitting or walking. Their buttocks can be sore when they sit and their feet have to readjust to walking and bearing weight. They will often develop painful blisters. Their balance is also affected and can take a few days to return to normal.[16]

DROPPING THINGS

One of the most common questions astronauts get asked is if they drop things when they get back to Earth. Dropping things happens a lot and it's usually when they go to pass something to someone else. They have forgotten the effects of gravity and are used to floating the object to someone.[17]

EVERYDAY OBJECTS ARE HEAVY

Things like apples, their phones, water bottles, the blankets they sleep under, their arms and even their heads all feel surprising heavy when astronauts are readjusting to gravity.

STRANGE SENSATIONS

Astronauts experience unique sensations to everyday events during readjustment. Walking up stairs feels more like pushing the stairs down rather than pushing their bodies up. Astronauts struggle to land after jumping because they feel like the ground is coming up too rapidly to meet them. They have problems turning corners while walking and even picking things up off of the ground is difficult.[18]

RE-ADJUSTING TO SLEEPING AT HOME

Some astronauts have reported the sensation of floating over their mattress for a few days after they return home, especially for those on long-duration missions.[19]

NOTES

1. Samantha Cristoforetti, *Diary of an Apprentice Astronaut*, trans. Jill Foulston (Penguin, 2020), 355, Kindle.

2. Cristoforetti, *Diary of an Apprentice Astronaut*, 368.

3. Mary Roach, *Packing for Mars: The Curious Science of Life in the Void* (New York, NY: WW Norton, 2011), 70.

4. Cristoforetti, *Diary of an Apprentice Astronaut*, 355.

5. "Robert Frost's Answer to Why Do Astronauts Directly Go to the Hospital after They Came from Space? – Quora," Quora, accessed May 31, 2021, https://qr.ae/pNJyoz.

6. Cristoforetti, *Diary of an Apprentice Astronaut*, 368.

7. Roach, *Packing for Mars*, 128.

8. Terry Virts, *How to Astronaut: An Insider's Guide to Leaving Planet Earth* (New York, Workman Publishing, 2020), 251.

9. "Expedition 48 Soyuz TMA-20M Landing," NASA, September 7, 2016, photograph, https://images.nasa.gov/details-nhq201609070009.

10. Tim Peake, *Ask an Astronaut: My Guide to Life in Space* (Little Brown and Company, 2017), 210.

11. Roach, *Packing for Mars*, 135.

12. Cristoforetti, *Diary of an Apprentice Astronaut*, 366.

13. Gary Jordan, "Houston, We Have a Podcast, Ep 140: Soyuz Landing," ed. Norah Moran, NASA (NASA, April 18, 2020), https://www.nasa.gov/johnson/HWHAP/soyuz-landing/.

14. Jordan, "Soyuz Landing."

15. Quora, "Why do Astronauts Directly go to the Hospital?."

16. Cristoforetti, *Diary of an Apprentice Astronaut*, 368.

17. Virts, *How to Astronaut*, 252-253.

18. "Astronaut Health and Performance - Spatial Disorientation: Which Way Is Down?," *Major Scientific Discoveries*, p. 373, accessed May 31, 2021, https://www.nasa.gov/centers/johnson/pdf/584739main_Wings-ch5d-pgs370-407.pdf.

19. "Sleeping in Space," CSA (Canadian Space Agency, August 22, 2019), https://www.asc-csa.gc.ca/eng/astronauts/living-in-space/sleeping-in-space.asp.

SPACEFLIGHT RECORDS

Russian Space Firsts

The Soviet Union is responsible for and holds the record for many spaceflight firsts.

FIRST HUMAN-MADE SATELLITE

On October 1, 1957, the Soviet Union became the first to send a human-made satellite into orbit. Sputnik 1, which in Russian means "satellite 1," launched the space race between the Soviets and the Americans. Sputnik 1 orbited Earth for almost three months before it re-entered Earth's atmosphere and became a shooting star on December 25, 1957.

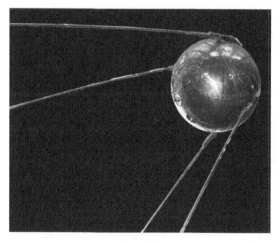

Replica of the first human-made satellite into orbit, Sputnik 1.
Photo courtesy of NASA.

FIRST MAN IN SPACE AND IN ORBIT

On April 12, 1961, cosmonaut Yuri Gagarin became the first human to launch into space and orbit the Earth onboard the spacecraft Vostok 1. From launch to landing, his entire journey lasted 1 hour and 58 minutes, or 118 minutes. It took 10 minutes to reach orbit. He spent

Cosmonaut Yuri Gagarin, the first human in space.
Photo courtesy of the Finnish Museum of Photography.

78 minutes in space. It took another 20 minutes to re-enter Earth's atmosphere. As planned, Yuri ejected from Vostok 1 and parachuted safely to Earth, which took another 10 minutes.[1]

Unlike today, where crews normally return to Earth inside their spacecraft, Yuri was ejected from the Vostok 1 capsule and parachuted to the ground. The early Soviet spacecrafts weren't built to land safely back on Earth, which is why early cosmonauts had extensive parachuting experience.

FIRST WOMAN IN SPACE

At the age of 26, cosmonaut Valentina Tereshkova became the first and the youngest woman, at that time, to travel into space in 1963. She orbited earth 48 times in just under three days. She only flew once, but her flight times added up to more than all of the American astronauts' flight time combined. Before she became a cosmonaut, Valentina was an experienced skydiver with more than 126 jumps under her belt.[2]

FIRST PEOPLE TO DIE IN SPACE

As of June 2022, the only people to die while in space, which is defined as above the Kármán line at 100,000 km or 330,000 feet above sea level, are cosmonauts Georgy Dobrovolsky, Viktor Patsayev, and Vladislav Volkov in June of 1971. After a three-week stay onboard space station Salyut 1, the crew onboard Soyuz 11 undocked to begin their journey back to earth. A cabin vent opened accidently during separation and the crew all died within seconds from decompression in space. The Soyuz 11 landed successfully on autopilot, but the crew were found dead. All space-bound crews wear pressurized suits during launch and re-entry now.[3]

Other Human Spaceflight Firsts

FIRST HUMANS TO TRAVEL BEYOND LOW EARTH ORBIT

Two months after the Soviets sent tortoises to the Moon and back, Apollo 8 launched on December 21, 1968 with three men onboard. American astronauts James Lovell, William Anders and Frank Borman were the first humans to leave Earth's low orbit, orbit the Moon, and return safely back on Earth.

FIRST HUMANS TO WITNESS AND PHOTOGRAPH THE EARTHRISE

On Christmas Eve in 1968, while orbiting the Moon onboard Apollo 8, William "Bill" Anders took a photo of the Earth rising above the Lunar horizon. This photo is known as "Earthrise" and is considered one of the most influential images of all time.

FIRST HUMANS TO LOSE CONTACT WITH EARTH

The Apollo 8 crew were the first humans to lose contact with Earth when they orbited the dark side of the Moon on December 24, 1968. As scheduled, the crew lost radio contact with Mission Control in Houston, Texas for 34 minutes.

Earthrise, taken on Dec. 24, 1968 by astronaut William Anders onboard Apollo 8. The orientation shown on the left is how the photo was originally taken. To "normalize it," the photo we are most familiar with has been rotated so that the Earth appears to be rising above the surface of the Moon. Image courtesy of NASA.[4]

FIRST MAN ON THE MOON

American astronauts Neil Armstrong and Buzz Aldrin were the first humans to land safely on the surface of the Moon, in July of 1969. Neil Armstrong was the first to step off the Lunar Module ladder and become the first human to step foot on the Moon.[5]

FIRST FATALITIES DURING LAUNCH

The Space Shuttle *Challenger* disintegrated 73 seconds after launch on the morning of January 28, 1986 and killed all seven crew members onboard. This was the 25th shuttle mission and was extra special due to the fact that Christa McAuliffe, a schoolteacher from New Hampshire, was onboard as part of a NASA program to send civilians into space. Many people watched the disaster happen live on TV, including many school children.[6]

FIRST ALL-WOMAN SPACEWALK & SPACEWALK BY TWO WOMEN

The first woman to spacewalk did so in July of 1984. It wasn't until October of 2019 that two women, astronauts Christina Koch and

Jessica Meir, performed the first all-woman spacewalk outside the International Space Station.[7]

FIRST SPACE TOURIST

In April of 2001, American entrepreneur Dennis Tito became the first person to pay their way to space. This was onboard the Russian Soyuz, which joined up with the International Space Station for a week-long stay.[8]

FIRST MARRIED COUPLE IN SPACE

American astronauts Jan Davis and Mark Lee met during astronaut training and married in 1991, but didn't tell NASA until after the ceremony. They launched together onboard Space Shuttle *Endeavor* in 1992. NASA now has an official policy to not send husbands and wives on the same space flight.[9]

Most Spaceflights

MOST SPACEFLIGHTS

American astronauts Franklin Chang-Diaz and Jerry Ross are tied for this record. They have both been to space seven times.

MOST LAUNCHES

Three men hold this record: American astronauts John W. Young, Jerry L. Ross, and Franklin Chang-Diaz have all launched seven times. However, Young launched from Earth six times and once from the Moon.

GREATEST VARIETY OF SPACE VEHICLES

Astronaut John W. Young has launched seven different times, but he's done it in four different space vehicles! He launched from Earth six times: twice on a Gemini, twice on an Apollo Command Module, and twice on the Space Shuttle. His seventh launch was from the Moon in the Apollo Lunar Module Ascent Stage.[10]

Duration Records

MOST TIME SPENT IN SPACE IN TOTAL

Cosmonaut Gennedy Padalka holds the record for spending the most time in space, with 878 days over the course of five flights. That means he spent two years, four months, three weeks, and five days in space. In fact, Russians hold the top eight spots for the most time in space. The ninth person in line for the longest time spent in space is American astronaut Peggy Whitson with 665 days in space spread out over three different flights.

LONGEST SINGLE SPACE FLIGHT

Russian cosmonaut Valeri Polyakov spent 437 days onboard the Mir space station. The next-longest single space flight belongs to cosmonaut Sergei Avdeyev who spent 379 days onboard Mir.

The record for longest single space flight by an American is held by Mark Vande Hei, who spent nearly a year in space with 355 days. Previously, NASA astronaut Scott Kelly held the record with 340 days. The longest space flight by a woman goes to Christina Koch at 328 days. Koch shattered this record in February 2020. Previously, Peggy Whitson had held the record since 2017 with 289 days.

LONGEST SOLO FLIGHT

Cosmonaut Valery Bykovsky was alone for 4 days and 23 hours during his solo spaceflight onboard Vostok 5 in June 1963.

LONGEST TIME SPENT ON THE MOON

Apollo 17 was the 11th and final Apollo mission. Astronauts Eugene Cernan and Harrison Schmitt spent over three days on the surface of the Moon. Their 74-hour, 59-minute, and 40-second Moon visit included three separate lunar EVAs.

LONGEST CONTINUOUS OCCUPATION OF SPACE

Space has continuously been occupied by humans since October 31, 2000, when Soyuz TM-31 launched from Earth and docked with the International Space Station.

LONGEST CONTINUOUS OCCUPATION OF A SPACECRAFT

The International Space Station has been continuously occupied by humans from 18 different countries and counting since November 2, 2000.[11]

 DID YOU KNOW?

LAST MAN ON THE MOON

It was custom that the Apollo mission commanders were the first ones out of the lunar modules and the last to get back in, which means Apollo 17's commander, Eugene "Gene" Cernan was the 11th out of 12 men to walk on the Moon, but is also the last person to have ever walked on the Moon.[12]

Speed and Altitude Records

FARTHEST HUMANS FROM EARTH

When the crew of Apollo 13 swung around the far side of the Moon in April 1970, they were 248,655 miles (400,171 km) away from Earth. That's a long way from home!

FASTEST HUMAN SPACEFLIGHT

Humans reached a top speed of 24,791 mph (39,897 kph) when the crew of Apollo 10 orbited the Moon in their CSM, named Charlie Brown, and headed back to Earth on May 26, 1969.[13]

Age Records

YOUNGEST PEOPLE IN SPACE

Before July 2021, Cosmonaut Gherman Titov was the youngest man to fly into space. He was 25 years old when he flew onboard Vostok 2 on August 6, 1961. Titov holds a number of other space firsts including the first to sleep, first to take photos from orbit and the first to film Earth from space. While Titov still holds the record for the youngest cosmonaut in space, he is no longer the youngest person to have flown into space. Oliver Daemen flew alongside Amazon's Jeff Bezos on the New Shepard spacecraft on July 20, 2021, and broke that record.[14]

Valentina Tershkova is not only the first woman to fly into space, she's also the youngest woman to fly into space. She was 26 years old when she flew onboard Vostok 6 in June 1963.

OLDEST MAN AND WOMAN IN SPACE

Until July 20, 2021, American astronaut John Glenn held the record for being the oldest person in space when he flew onboard the space shuttle on October 29, 1998, when he was 77 years old.

And American astronaut Peggy Whitson was 56 years old when she flew into space on November 17, 2016. She turned 57 in space on February 9, 2017, setting the record for being the oldest woman in space.

But on July 20, 2021, 82-year-old pilot Wally Funk, originally one of the Mercury 13 women, flew into space alongside Amazon's Jeff Bezos on Blue Origin's New Shepard. That feat broke the record for both the oldest person in space and the oldest woman in space.[15]

The record was broken again on October 12, 2021, by Star Trek star William Shatner at the age of 90 when he flew into space onboard Blue Origin's New Shepard spacecraft.

OLDEST PERSON TO WALK ON THE MOON

Alan Shepard set several records during his astronaut career: the first American to fly into space (in 1961), having the shortest space flight in history (15 minutes), and being the first person to pee in his spacesuit. He set another record when he flew to the Moon as part of Apollo 14 in 1971, becoming the oldest person to walk on the Moon—at the age of 47.[16]

YOUNGEST PERSON TO WALK ON THE MOON

At the age of 36, Charlie Duke was the youngest person to walk on the Moon.

Spacewalk Records

FIRST SPACEWALK

Cosmonaut Alexei (Alexey) Leonov became the first person to spacewalk in 1965. He spent 12 minutes floating outside, attached to his Voskhod 2 with a 16-foot (4.8-meter) umbilical cable.

FIRST WOMAN TO SPACEWALK

On July 24th, 1984, cosmonaut Svetlana Savitskaya became the first woman to perform a spacewalk, outside the Salyut 7 space station. During her 3-hour and 35-minute EVA she helped cut and weld metal pieces in space. While she was the first woman to spacewalk, she remains the only female cosmonaut to spacewalk, even after all of these years.

FIRST UNTETHERED SPACEWALK

While the first spacewalk honor goes to the Soviets, the first untethered spacewalk belongs to American astronaut Bruce McCandless II. During the 10th space shuttle mission, on Feb 7, 1984, McCandless tested the MMU jetpack, reaching a distance of 328 feet (100 m) away from Space Shuttle *Challenger*. That's more than the length of an American football field, which measures 300 feet (91 m).

FIRST DEEP SPACEWALK

American astronaut Al Worden became the first person to spacewalk outside of Earth's low orbit as part of the Apollo 15 mission in 1971. His walk lasted 39 minutes and took place 198,800 miles (320,000 km) from Earth.

MOST SPACEWALKS

Cosmonaut Anatoly Solovyev holds the record with 16 different spacewalks, with a total of 82 hours and 21 minutes of EVA time.

Astronaut Peggy Whitson holds the record for the most spacewalks by a woman, with 10 separate spacewalks. Her total EVA time is 60 hours and 21 minutes.

Bruce McCandless II during the first untethered spacewalk. Photo courtesy of NASA.

LONGEST SINGLE SPACEWALK

Astronauts James Voss and Susan Helms both hold the record for the longest single spacewalk. Their spacewalk lasted 8 hours and 56 minutes as they worked to assemble the International Space Station in March of 2001.

Out-of-This-World Records

FIRST PERSON TO VOMIT IN SPACE

The first person to vomit was actually not the first person in space. Cosmonaut Gherman Titov threw up while in Vostok II.

Space sickness wasn't common in the early days of spaceflights, probably because there was very little room to move around in their tiny capsules. Space sickness can be made worse in larger spaces, especially since it involves head movement.

FIRST PERSON TO SLEEP IN SPACE

Cosmonaut Gherman Titov slept onboard Vostok II during his 25-hour flight in August 1961. He woke up to find his arms floating in front of him, which could have been a problem with so many crucial switches nearby.

FIRST PERSON TO RELIEVE HIMSELF ON THE MOON

After Neil Armstrong had taken his "One small step for man, one giant leap for mankind," and was off collecting a contingency moondust sample, his Apollo 11 crewmember Buzz Aldrin urinated into a special collection bag within his spacesuit while still on the Lunar Module ladder.[17]

FIRST PEOPLE TO SHOWER IN SPACE

The three crews of three astronauts who were onboard the US space station *Skylab* between May 14th, 1973 and July 11th, 1979, all enjoyed a shower in space. This special shower had a ring on the floor that the user would stand inside. A circular curtain could be lifted and attached to the ceiling. A hose would spray 3 quarts (2.8 liters) of water that would be sucked up afterwards with a special vacuum cleaner.

FIRST PERSON TO MAKE AN ORBIT OF EARTH ON A BICYCLE

American astronaut Alan Bean, who also walked on the Moon during Apollo 12, spent just over 90 minutes on a stationary bike onboard space station *Skylab* in 1973. It takes about 90 minutes to orbit Earth and Alan pedaled during the entire orbit!

FIRST PERSON TO GET MARRIED WHILE IN SPACE

Cosmonaut Yuri Malenchenko is known for a lot of things, including

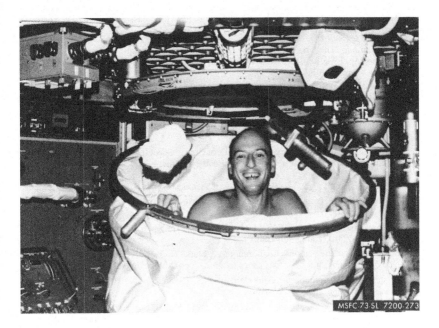

Astronaut Charles Conrad, Jr., after a shower onboard Skylab. Photo courtesy of NASA.[18]

flying to space five times and spending a total of 641 days in space. But he's also the only person to have gotten married while in space. Onboard the International Space Station in 2003, he and his bride, Ekaterina, had a special videoconference where they exchanged their vows.[19]

NOTES

1. "Robert Frost's Answer to When Yuri Gagarin Went into Space, the Journey Took 108 Minutes. Now I Am Confused Whether He Spent 108 Minutes in Space or Did the Whole Journey Take 108 Minutes? – Quora," Quora, accessed June 1, 2021, https://qr.ae/pNQleg.

2. "Pioneering Women in Space: A Gallery of Astronaut Firsts," Space.com, March 8, 2021, https://www.space.com/16143-women-space-firsts-gallery.html.

3. "Space Deaths Detailed," *The Leader-Post*, November 3, 1973, https://news.google.com/newspapers?id=AfhUAAAAIBAJ&pg=4921,564442.

4. William Anders, *Earthrise, Taken on Dec. 24, 1968 by Astronaut William Anders Onboard Apollo 8.*, NASA (NASA, December 24, 1968), https://www.hq.nasa.gov/office/pao/History/alsj/a410/AS8-14-2383HR.jpg.

5. Brian Dunbar, "The First Person on the Moon," ed. Shelley Canright, NASA (NASA, last modified April 9, 2009), https://www.nasa.gov/audience/forstudents/k-4/stories/first-person-on-moon.html.

6. Richard Webb, "Has Anyone Ever Died in Space?," New Scientist, accessed June 1, 2021, https://www.newscientist.com/question/anyone-ever-died-space/.

7. Maya Wei-Haas, "First All-Woman Space Walk Puts Spotlight on Spacesuit Design," National Geographic, October 18, 2019, https://www.nationalgeographic.com/science/article/first-all-women-spacewalk-suit-design.

8. Mike Wall, "Giant Leaps: Biggest Milestones of Human Spaceflight," Space.com, September 12, 2011, https://www.space.com/11329-human-spaceflight-biggest-moments-50th-anniversary/2.html.

9. "Love Is in the Air: Great Couples of Aerospace History," National Air and Space Museum, February 14, 2018, https://airandspace.si.edu/stories/editorial/love-air-great-couples-aerospace-history.

10. "John W. Young Biography," NASA, December 2018, https://www.nasa.gov/sites/default/files/atoms/files/young_john.pdf.

11. Brian Dunbar, "International Cooperation," ed. Mark Garcia, NASA (NASA, October 15, 2020), https://www.nasa.gov/mission_pages/station/cooperation/index.html.

12. Brian Dunbar, "Remembering Gene Cernan," NASA (NASA, October 20, 2017), https://www.nasa.gov/astronautprofiles/cernan.

13. Mike Wall, "The Most Extreme Human Spaceflight Records," Space.com, April 23, 2019, https://www.space.com/11337-human-spaceflight-records-50th-anniversary.html.

14. Elizabeth Howell, "Blue Origin to Launch Its 1st Astronaut Flight with Jeff Bezos and Crew of 3 Today," Space.com (Space, July 20, 2021), https://www.space.com/blue-origin-jeff-bezos-first-human-flight-launch-day.

15. Howell, "Blue Origin to Launch Its 1st Astronaut Flight."

16. Wall, "The Most Extreme Human Spaceflight Records."

17. *Buzz Aldrin, 1st Man to Pee on the Moon*, YouTube (Opie Radio, 2016), https://youtu.be/4V3QL5EbBzA.

18. "Skylab shower," NASA, June 1, 1973, photograph, https://images.nasa.gov/details-7042918.

19. Scott Kelly, *Endurance: A Year in Space, A Lifetime of Discovery* (New York: Alfred A. Knopf, 2017), 326.

RANDOM SPACE FACTS

Seeing Spots
COSMIC RAY VISUAL PHENOMENON
Since the Apollo era, many astronauts have noticed this phenomenon, also known as light flashes (LF), where cosmic flashes occasionally occur and light up their field of vision, even when their eyes are closed. Not all astronauts see them.

It's believed to be the result of radiation striking the retina and creating the illusion of light. While there are several theories why this happens, the cause of this phenomenon still isn't thoroughly understood. Astronauts who have seen them have said that the light flashes appear in the shapes of spots, stars, streaks, blobs, and comets.

FLASHES OF COLOR
These cosmic ray light flashes have shown up in a variety of colors. Astronauts have seen them appear in yellow, pale green, orange, and red. But the most common colors are white and blue. Astronauts on Lunar missions almost always reported white flashes.

COUNTING FLASHES BEFORE BED
Light flashes seem to happen more often before astronauts fall asleep. Astronauts on the Lunar missions reported seeing light flashes every 2.9 minutes, on average. For other missions, astronauts report seeing them once every 6.8 minutes.

SEEING SPOTS OVER THE WEAK SPOT
Earth has a weak spot in the magnetic field over what is known as the South Atlantic Anomaly, or SAA. Due to this weak spot, this area is filled with a high level of cosmic radiation. Astronauts have reported that they see the "white flashes" more when the International Space station flies over this area.[1]

Smells in Space

FORBIDDEN FOOD

After learning from bad experiences, NASA created a "banned food" list to help reduce the amount of smelly bodily gasses on the Apollo missions, the space shuttle and International Space Station. This list included foods like beans, cabbage, Brussels sprouts and broccoli.

According to Dr. Charles Bourland, retired long time director of the space food program and author of *The Astronaut's Cookbook: Tales, Recipes, and More*,[2] beans were not used until the Shuttle era.[3]

HOW TO REDUCE FARTS IN SPACE AND ON EARTH

The Russians seem to know a lot about this topic. The Russian diet consists mainly of potatoes, cabbage and vodka, but also a lot of dill. The secret is the dill. This spice reduces bloating and gas.

THE SMELL OF SPACE

Astronauts describe the smell of space like a strong burned metal smell, like the smell of welding or the smell of sparklers. Objects that have been exposed to the vacuum of space have this same unique smell about them.

DESIGNED TO MINIMIZE SMELLS

Much like everything on the International Space Station is designed to be fireproof, everything is also designed to minimize smells and prevent materials from off-gassing.[4]

Random

FIREFLIES OR SNOWFLAKES IN SPACE?

During the first of John Glenn's three orbits, he looked out the window and saw a series of small luminescent specks surrounding the capsule. In an effort to describe what they looked like, he called them fireflies and when he tried banging on the side of the capsule, they moved. No one knew what they were. NASA scientists were worried the sparks meant there was something malfunctioning.

Astronaut Scott Carpenter flew into space on the next Mercury mission and he also saw the "fireflies", or "snowflakes" as he called them. He quickly realized they were tiny white frost particles that had come from the frozen condensation on the side of the capsule. Condensation would build up on the outside of the capsule and would freeze as it passed from the sunlight into the cold darkness. Then when the spacecraft would come again into the sunlight, the frost particles would come off and float around the capsule. The sun would illuminate the flakes which would make them look luminescent.[5]

VIDEO CALL WITH ANYONE YOU WANT

One of the many perks of being an astronaut while in space is being able to have a video call with almost anyone. Want to chat with your favorite celebrity? The President? Your rock star idol? Done. NASA will set up two video chats with whomever you want. Most everyone accepts.[6]

COSMONAUTS ARE AWARDED MEDALS

Russian cosmonauts are awarded a very special medal when they return home. They all receive the Hero of the Soviet Union Star.[7]

HUMAN SKULL ONBOARD SPACE SHUTTLE ATLANTIS

It's not every day you get to share your work space with a human skull, but the lucky crew onboard Space Shuttle *Atlantis* did. The skull was sent up in order to learn how much radiation penetrates astronauts' heads while in low Earth orbit.[8]

PHANTOM HUMAN TORSO

Imagine getting up in the middle of the night to use the space toilet and bumping into a phantom human torso. Well, that has happened, and it's almost scared the pee out of some astronauts. It's all in the name of science. NASA sent up a dummy human torso that has the same radiation resistance as a real human torso. It has radiation detectors both on the inside and outside that measure what type of radiation astronauts are being exposed to.

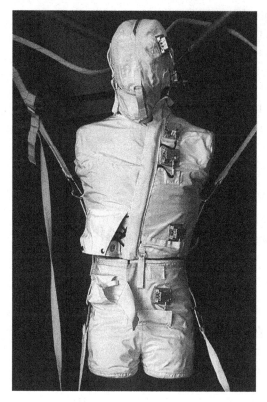

The Phantom Torso has over 350 radiation measuring devices. Photo courtesy of NASA.

MEASURING RADIATION IN SPACE

Besides sending fake and real body parts to space, NASA has other, less creepy ways to measure radiation while astronauts are in space. Astronauts have little radiation badges that they'll wear and can eventually turn black. They also have little computer chips that measure radiation levels they are subjected to the entire time they're in space. Radiation levels can then be counted once they return home and turn the chips in.[9]

FOOD IN YOUR SLEEPING BAG TO KEEP WARM

Astronaut Marsha Ivins enjoyed sleeping in the airlock of the space shuttle when she was in space. It was like her own private bedroom, but it was the coldest part of the shuttle by about 20 degrees. She would tuck her arms into her sleeping bag, wear four layers of clothes, and warm up a package of food in the oven and sleep with it in her bag like you would with a hot-water bottle.[10]

Taken to Space

LUKE SKYWALKER'S LIGHTSABER

In 2007, to commemorate the 30th anniversary of the release of the original *Star Wars* film in 1977, Lucasfilm collaborated with the Johnson Space Center and arranged for the original lightsaber prop to be taken into space.[11]

MY SIGNATURE FLEW IN SPACE

On one of her three space shuttle flights, astronaut Rhea Seddon flew the signatures of every student in her hometown on a long roll of calculator tape. This meant that they could all say their signature had flown in space.[12]

COPIES OF THE APOLLO 12 MISSION PLAQUE

The crew of Apollo 12 wanted a special memento to remember their trip to the Moon so they had four thin aluminum light-weight copies of the mission plaque made. They brought them along to the Moon and when they returned, three of the copies went to the Apollo 12 astronauts, one each for Charles "Pete" Conrad Jr., Richard Gordon and Alan Bean. The fourth copy went to the man who made the copies, Jack Kinzler, who happened to be Conrad's next-door neighbor.[13]

GORILLA SUIT

Astronaut Scott Kelly, who spent nearly a year in space, was sent a vacuum-packed gorilla suit by his twin brother, Mark. Scott dressed up as Space Gorilla and hid in fellow astronaut Tim Kopra's crew quarters and probably scared the space pudding out of him when he opened the door. The suit spread a lot of joy and laughter, not just in the American side of the ISS, but in the Russian side as well.

Kelly and crewmate Tim Peake made a short video that involved a stowaway gorilla that chases Tim up and down the US lab with the *Benny Hill* theme song, "Yakety Sax" and it goes viral. It helped bring joy and new attention and interest to what they're doing on the space station.[14]

FAMILY PHOTOS & PICTURES OF COWS

Shuttle astronauts were allowed to take two personal items with them that could be brought out of their personal lockers while in flight. Most everyone took a picture of their family with them, except one astronaut who was single and brought a photo of his cows. Bumper stickers were also a popular item that allowed crew members to decorate their surroundings while in space.[15]

BUMPER STICKERS

Several astronauts took bumper stickers that represented which branch of the military the astronauts favored, things like "Beat Army," "Beat Navy," "Air Force: A Great Way of Life." Astronaut Judy Resnik, the second American astronaut in space, took an "I Love Tom Selleck" sticker for her shuttle locker.[16]

CUSTOM LEGO FIGURINES

In 2011, when NASA launched the Juno space probe to orbit Jupiter, it carried three LEGO figurines, one of Galileo Galilei, one of the Roman god Jupiter and the third of Juno, Jupiter's wife.[17]

AMELIA EARHART'S WRISTWATCH

In 1928, Amelia Earhart was the first woman to cross the Atlantic by plane. She made another historic flight when she flew nonstop across the Atlantic solo four years later in 1932. She was instrumental in creating a group for women pilots called The Ninety-Nines. On both of her solo flights, Amelia wore a wristwatch that was a Longines one-button, two-register chronograph.

After her 1932 solo Atlantic crossing, she met H. Gordon Selfridge Jr., the owner of the famous London department store that shares his

Three LEGO figurines onboard the Juno spacecraft. Left to Right: Galileo Galilei, the Roman goddess Juno and Jupiter, husband of Juno. Photo courtesy of NASA/JPL-Caltech/LEGO

name. Selfridge and Earhart became friends when she realized she'd need appropriate clothing for public appearances. Selfridge gave her a special watch, which she was wearing when she disappeared on her last flight. Earhart gave Selfridge her watch in exchange.

After Earhart was presumed dead, Selfridge gave the watch to Fay Gillis Wells, a member of the Ninety-Nines, in 1963. Wells held onto it until she founded the Forest of Friendship to honor other individuals in aviation. To raise money for the Forest of Friendship in Amelia's hometown, she auctioned off the watch. Joan Kerwin, the director The Ninety-Nines, bought it. Kerwin held onto it until 2009 when it was presented to another Ninety-Nines member, astronaut Shannon Walker. 82 years to the day after its first flight, Shannon took Amelia's watch with her to the International Space Station. While the watch still works, Shannon didn't use it to keep time, but did keep it with her during her mission.[18] After Shannon returned, the watch was placed on display in the Ninety-Nines Museum of Women Pilots in Oklahoma City.[19]

A PIECE OF THE WRIGHT BROTHERS' FIRST AIRPLANE

Less than 70 years after the Wright Brothers flew their first airplane, mankind flew to the Moon. To link two of humankind's great achievements, astronaut Neil Armstrong carried a few scraps of fabric and wood from the Wright Brothers' first plane, the Wright Flyer, also known as "Kitty Hawk," to the surface of the Moon and back with him.

North Carolina native and astronaut Michael Smith, assigned as pilot, took a piece of wood and fabric from the Wright Flyer with him onboard the Space Shuttle *Challenger* on January 28, 1986. These pieces never made it to space because the shuttle broke apart 72 seconds after liftoff, killing everyone onboard. The Wright Flyer fragments were recovered from the wreck of the shuttle and are on display at the North Carolina Museum of History.[20]

Most recently, pieces of the Wright Brothers' famous plane have reached even farther than the Moon. Pieces of Wright Flyer have now flown on Mars. The robotic solar helicopter named Ingenuity has a small piece of the Wright Flyer's wing fabric—about the size of a postage stamp—attached to a cable underneath the solar panel. Ingenuity made history when it became the first vehicle to perform a controlled atmospheric flight on Mars on April 19, 2021.[21]

A small swatch of unbleached muslin material that was used on the Wright brothers' first airplane. It measures 0.5-inch x 0.5 inch (1.3 x 1.3 centimeters). Photo courtesy of NASA/ JPL-Caltech [21]

Buzz Lightyear, Pixar's space ranger, spent over a year onboard the International Space Station. Photo courtesy of NASA.

BUZZ LIGHTYEAR–TO THE ISS AND BEYOND

Pixar's Buzz Lightyear made his way to space onboard the International Space Station. In May 2008, a 12-inch Buzz Lightyear action figure was launched onboard the Space Shuttle *Discovery*. The *"Toy Story"* space ranger spent over 15 months in space as part of the Toys in Space educational program.[23] This little space ranger has spent more time on the ISS on one mission than any astronaut or cosmonaut. He returned home September 11, 2009, on Space Shuttle *Discovery*.[24]

NOTES

1. Terry Virts, *How to Astronaut: An Insider's Guide to Leaving Planet Earth* (New York, Workman Publishing, 2020), 233.

2. Find the book on Amazon or where other fine books are sold: https://www.amazon.com/Astronauts-Cookbook-Tales-Recipes-More/dp/1441906231

3. Mary Roach, *Packing for Mars: The Curious Science of Life in the Void* (New York, NY: WW Norton, 2011), 305.

4. Tim Peake, *Ask an Astronaut: My Guide to Life in Space* (Little Brown and Company, 2017), 223.

5. Nancy Atkinson, "The Mystery of John Glenn's Fireflies Returns," Universe Today, January 5, 2015, https://www.universetoday.com/82211/the-mystery-of-john-glenns-fireflies-returns/.

6. Terry Virts, *How to Astronaut: An Insider's Guide to Leaving Planet Earth* (New York, Workman Publishing, 2020), 163.

7. Roach, *Packing for Mars*, 74

8. Roach, *Packing for Mars*, 145

9. Chris Hadfield, "The ISS: Experiments," MasterClass (MasterClass), accessed June 1, 2021, https://www.masterclass.com/classes/chris-hadfield-teaches-space-exploration/chapters/the-iss-experiments.

10. Marsha Ivans and Caitlin Roper, "An Astronaut Reveals What Life in Space Is Really Like," Wired (Conde Nast, November 19, 2014), https://www.wired.com/2014/11/marsha-ivins/.

11. Dr Alex Baker, "The 10 Most Unusual Objects Ever Launched into Space," Sent into Space, March 20, 2020, https://www.sentintospace.com/post/the-10-most-unusual-objects-ever-launched-into-space.

12. Rhea Seddon, "You CAN Take It With You!," AstronautRheaSeddon.com, October 3, 2019, https://astronautrheaseddon.com/you-can-take-it-with-you/.

13. Brian Dunbar, "The Personal Preference Kit: What Astronauts Take With Them To Space," ed. Thalia Patrinos, NASA (NASA, last modified November 18, 2020), https://www.nasa.gov/feature/the-personal-preference-kit-what-astronauts-take-with-them-to-space.

14. Scott Kelly, *Endurance: A Year in Space, A Lifetime of Discovery* (New York: Alfred A. Knopf, 2017), 345.

15. Seddon, "You CAN Take It With You."

16. *View of Mission Specialist Judith Resnik Sitting on the Floor of the Middeck. Beside Her Is a [Sticker] Which Reads "I Love Tom Selleck".* (NASA, September 8, 1984), https://science.ksc.nasa.gov/mirrors/images/images/pao/STS41D/10061568.jpg.

17. Brian Dunbar, "Juno Spacecraft to Carry Three Figurines to Jupiter Orbit," NASA (NASA, last modified August 7, 2017), https://www.nasa.gov/mission_pages/juno/news/lego20110803.html.

18. Robert Z. Pearlman, "Amelia Earhart's Watch Reaches Space Station 82 Years After Historic Flight," Space.com, June 18, 2010, https://www.space.com/8631-amelia-earhart-watch-reaches-space-station-82-years-historic-flight.html.

19. "The Amelia Earhart Watch," expertswatches.com, accessed June 1, 2021, https://expertswatches.com/pages/the-amelia-earhart-watch.

20. "Full-Size Replica Wright Flyer Featured at N.C. Transportation Museum," NC Cultural Resources Newsroom, accessed June 1, 2021, https://web.archive.org/web/20120426044500/http://news.ncdcr.gov/2009/12/10/full-size-replica-wright-flyer-featured-at-nc-transportation-museum/.

21. Mike Wall, "Mars Helicopter Ingenuity Carries Piece of Wright Brothers' Famous Plane," Space.com, March 24, 2021, https://www.space.com/mars-helicopter-ingenuity-wright-brothers-plane.

22. "Pride of the West – and Mars," April 6, 2021, NASA, https://images.nasa.gov/details-PIA24438.

23. Baker, "The 10 Most Unusual Objects Ever Launched into Space."

24. Space.com Staff, "Cosmic Toy Story: Buzz Lightyear in Space (Photos)," Space.com, August 14, 2013, https://www.space.com/19384-buzz-lightyear-toys-space-photos.html.

QUIZ YOURSELF

1. What foods are banned from the International Space Station?
   A. Diet soda
   B. Freeze-dried Astronaut Ice Cream
   C. Bread
   D. All of the above
   E. None of the above

2. Astronauts wear adult diapers during spacewalks.
   A. True
   B. False

3. Which one is NOT a cosmonaut tradition that happens before launch?
   A. Plant a tree
   B. Pee on the rear-right tire of the bus
   C. Get a haircut
   D. Eat steak and eggs for breakfast

4. How many sunsets do the astronauts and cosmonauts onboard the ISS experience every day?
   A. 24
   B. 16
   C. 1
   D. 18

5. What are the two official languages onboard the International Space Station?
   A. English and Mandarin
   B. English and Russian
   C. Russian and Italian
   D. Russian and Mandarin

6. During long-duration space expeditions, astronauts can grow up to 2 ½ inches (6.35 cm).
A. True
B. False

7. Astronauts don't actually drink Tang while onboard the International Space Station?
A. True
B. False

8. Who was the first person to spacewalk?
A. Alan Shephard
B. Yuri Gagarin
C. Alexey Leonov
D. Sally Ride

9. The Olympic Torch has been to space.
A. True
B. False

10. Systems onboard the ISS can recycle over 90% of the crew's urine and sweat into purified water.
A. True
B. False

11. Which of the following is NOT one of the things astronauts can experience after returning to Earth?
A. Dropping things
B. Earth sickness
C. Feeling like they are floating over their mattress
D. None of the above
E. All of the above

12. You would find a body bag and birth control onboard the International Space Station.
  A. True
  B. False

13. What does space smell like according to those who have been to space?
  A. Cotton candy
  B. Buttered popcorn like at the movie theatre
  C. Campfire smoke
  D. Strong burned metal smell, like the smell of welding or the smell of sparklers

14. Which musical instrument has NOT been played in space?
  A. Saxophone
  B. Guitar
  C. Bagpipes
  D. Banjo

15. What was the most played song used to wake up the space shuttle crews?
  A. "Top of the World" by The Carpenters
  B. "What a Wonderful World" by Louis Armstrong
  C. "Star Wars Theme" by John Williams
  D. "Rocket Man (I Think It's Going To Be a Long, Long Time" by Elton John

16. What was the first item to be lost in space by an astronaut?
  A. Camera
  B. Wedding ring
  C. Needle-nose pliers
  D. A glove

17. No one has died while in space.
   A. True
   B. False

18. Which of these injuries and ailments have NOT happened to astronauts while in space?
   A. Developing "lizard feet"
   B. Nerve pain
   C. Losing fingernails
   D. Runny nose

19. Astronauts send urine and stool samples back to Earth to be studied.
   A. True
   B. False

20. Astronauts send their dirty clothes back to Earth in cargo ships that burn up in the atmosphere like a shooting star.
   A. True
   B. False

QUIZ ANSWERS

1. What foods are banned from the International Space Station?
   A. Diet soda
   B. Freeze-dried Astronaut Ice Cream
   C. Bread
   D. All of the above
   E. None of the above

2. Astronauts wear adult diapers during spacewalks.
   A. True
   B. False

3. Which one is NOT a cosmonaut tradition that happens before launch?
   A. Plant a tree
   B. Pee on the rear-right tire of the bus
   C. Get a haircut
   D. Eat steak and eggs for breakfast

4. How many sunsets do the astronauts and cosmonauts onboard the ISS experience every day?
   A. 24
   B. 16
   C. 1
   D. 18

5. What are the two official languages onboard the International Space Station?
   A. English and Mandarin
   B. English and Russian
   C. Russian and Italian
   D. Russian and Mandarin

6. During long-duration space expeditions, astronauts can grow up to 2 ½ inches (6.35 cm)?
   A. True
   B. False

7. Astronauts don't actually drink Tang while onboard the International Space Station?
   A. True
   B. False

8. Who was the first person to spacewalk?
   A. Alan Shephard
   B. Yuri Gagarin
   C. Alexey Leonov
   D. Sally Ride

9. The Olympic Torch has been to space.
   A. True
   B. False

10. Systems onboard the ISS can recycle over 90% of the crew's urine and sweat into purified water.
   A. True
   B. False

11. Which of the following is NOT one of the things astronauts can experience after returning to Earth?
   A. Dropping things
   B. Earth sickness
   C. Feeling like they are floating over their mattress
   C. None of the above
   E. All of the above

12. You would find a body bag and birth control onboard the International Spaces Station.

A. True
B. False

13. What does space smell like according to those who have been to space?

A. Cotton candy
B. Buttered popcorn like at the movie theatre
C. Campfire smoke
D. Strong burned metal smell, like the smell of welding or the smell of sparkler

14. Which musical instrument has NOT been played in space?

A. Saxophone
B. Guitar
C. Bagpipes
D. Banjo

15. What was the most played song used to wake up the space shuttle crews?

A. "Top of the World" by The Carpenters
B. "What a Wonderful World" by Louis Armstrong
C. "Star Wars Theme" by John Williams
D. "Rocket Man (I Think It's Going To Be a Long, Long Time" by Elton John

16. What was the first item to be lost in space by an astronaut?

A. Camera
B. Wedding ring
C. Needle-nose pliers
D. A glove

17. No one has died while in space.

A. True
B. False

18. Which of these injuries and ailments have NOT happened to astronauts while in space?

A. Developing "lizard feet"
B. Nerve pain
C. Losing fingernails
D. Runny nose

19. Astronauts send urine and stool samples back to Earth to be studied.

A. True
B. False

20. Astronauts send their dirty clothes back to Earth in cargo ships that burn up in the atmosphere like a shooting star.

A. True
B. False

GLOSSARY OF TERMS & ACRONYMS

ARED (Advanced Resistance Exercise Device)
The name of the weightless weightlifting machine astronauts use while on the space station to help counteract the bone density and muscle mass loss that occurs from living in microgravity.

AQUARIUS
The world's only undersea research station, laboratory, and habitat used in NEEMO. Aquarius is where NASA sends groups of astronauts, engineers, and scientists to live and train for up to three weeks to prepare them for future space missions.

Located 3.5 miles (5.6 km) off Key Largo, Florida in the Florida Keys, it sits on the ocean floor 62 feet (19 m) below the surface.

CAPCOM
Shortened acronym for Capsule Communicator. The role in Mission Control, normally filled by an astronaut, who is responsible for talking to the astronauts in space.

CAVES
Acronym for Cooperative Adventure for Valuing and Exercising Human Behavior and Performance Skills. This is an ESA astronaut training course in cave environments that takes place over several days. It simulates a space-like environment where astronauts carry out exploration activities that help them develop and practice efficiency, cooperation and risk management with their crew members.

CEVIS (Cycle Ergometer with Vibration Isolation and Stabilization)
This is the stationary bicycle the astronauts use for cardiovascular training on the ISS.

CSA
Acronym for Canadian Space Agency. The Canadian equivalent of NASA, ESA, JAXA and Roscosmos.

CO_2
Carbon Dioxide. This chemical compound is what we breathe

out and what needs to be removed from spacesuits and the space station.

CSL

Acronym for Crew Support Laptops. These are one of two laptops kept in the crew's quarters onboard the ISS. It's the computer that allows them to connect to a computer in Houston remotely to then access the internet.

CEVIS

Acronym for Cycle Ergometer with Vibration Isolation and Stabilization. This is the stationary bike with no seat that astronauts use while on the International Space Station.

CYGNUS

One of the resupply cargo spacecrafts that flies to the ISS. It was developed by the American company Northrop Grumman Innovation Systems, formally Orbital ATK. The Cygnus cargo ships have been flying on behalf of NASA since 2013.

DPC (Daily Planning Conference)

Each workday on the ISS, there are two DPCs, one in the morning and one in the evening. It's a meeting held via radio between the ISS astronauts and cosmonauts and mission control centers around the world.

DRAGON

SpaceX's spacecraft that comes in two varieties: Crew Dragon and Cargo Dragon. It has carried cargo to the ISS on behalf of NASA since 2012. It has launched crews to the ISS since May 2020.

EMU (Extravehicular Mobility Unit)

This is the pressurized American spacesuit astronauts use while performing spacewalks.

ERA

Acronym for the European Robotic Arm developed by ESA for the International Space Station.

ESA

Acronym for European Space Agency. The European equivalent of NASA, CSA, JAXA and Roscosmos.

EUROCOM

This is the name of the CAPCOM position at the Columbus Control Center or Col-CC responsible for speaking with the ISS astronauts on the

Space-to-Ground radio, usually about activities in the ESA Columbus module.

EVA (Extravehicular Activity)
This is what most people call a spacewalk while wearing a pressurized spacesuit.

FLUID SHIFT
The shifting and redistribution of bodily fluids caused by weightlessness.

FOD (Foreign Object Debris)
Once spaceships enter microgravity, FOD come out of hiding and make its appearance. FOD can be tiny nuts and bolts, metal shavings, staples, hair, dust or plastic flotsam. There are people at the Kennedy Space Center whose entire job is to keep the spacecrafts clean and FOD-free.

G
G used in this book refers to a unit of measurement for the perceived weight felt in a spacecraft. For reference, 1 G is equal to a person's or object's normal weight on the Earth's surface.

GLAVNI
The name of the CAPCOM position at the Tsentr

Upravleniya Poloyotami (TsUP) or mission control center near Moscow, Russia responsible for speaking with the ISS astronauts on Space-to-Ground radio.

ISS
Acronym for the International Space Station.

JAXA
Acronym for Japanese Space Agency. The Japanese equivalent of NASA, ESA, CSA and Roscosmos.

J-COM
The name of the CAPCOM position at the Control Center of the Japanese Space Agency responsible for speaking with the ISS astronauts on Space-to-Ground radio, usually about activities in the Japanese module JEM.

JEM
Acronym for the Japanese Experiment Module on the ISS.

MAG
NASA's acronym for the Maximum Absorbency Garment, or adult diapers, the astronauts use during launch, re-entry and spacewalks.

MECO

Abbreviation for Main Engine Cutoff and pronounced as "mee-ko."

MICROGRAVITY

The condition where people and objects appear to be weightless and float in space because they are in free fall. Microgravity doesn't mean zero gravity or the absence of gravity. It means there is a small amount of gravity, but in orbit everything is in free fall and falling at the same rate. Since everything is all falling together, everything appears to float when compared with the spacecraft.

MMU

Acronym for Manned Maneuvering Unit. The MMU was an earlier jet-pack before the SAFER jet-pack. It contained enough propellant for a six-hour EVA depending on how much maneuvering is done.

NASA

Acronym for National Aeronautics and Space Administration, the American space agency. The American equivalent to CSA, ESA, JAXA and Roscosmos.

NBL (Neutral Buoyancy Laboratory)

This is NASA's training facility with a giant pool where astronauts wear the EMU suit and train for EVAs. At the bottom are real-size models of the non-Russian modules of the ISS.

NEEMO (NASA Extreme Environment Mission Operations)

This is a NASA program in the Florida Keys where astronauts, engineers and scientists are sent to an underwater laboratory called Aquarius, for missions up to three weeks. They conduct experiments, test technology and simulate how things might work in space.

ORLAN

This is the name of Russian's pressurized spacesuit used for EVAs. Orlan in Russian means "sea eagle."

PAYCOM

The name for the CAPCOM position at the Payload Operations Center at NASA's Marshal Space Flight Center in Huntsville, Alabama that is responsible for speaking with the ISS astronauts on Space-to-Ground radio, usually about NASA experiments.

PLSS

Acronym for Portable Life Support System, or backpack, that incorporates a small jet-pack that is worn as part of an astronaut's spacesuit.

PROGRESS

Russia's cargo vehicle and the twin of the Soyuz.

RMS

Acronym for Remote Manipulator System, which are robotic arms like the Canadarm2 or Dextre, that are used to capture and release satellites, free-floating cargo spacecrafts, and help maneuver spacewalking astronauts.

ROSCOSMOS

The name of the Russian space agency. The Russian equivalent of NASA, CSA, ESA and JAXA.

SAFER

Acronym for Simplified Aid for EVA Rescue. This small jet-pack is incorporated into the PLSS, which is a new and improved version of the MMU. This jet-pack relies on small nitrogen-jet thrusters that allow an astronaut to maneuver in space in case they become detached from the space station during a spacewalk.

The SAFER jet-pack comes with 24 high-pressure thrusters that give control in six axes – pitch, roll, yaw, forwards/backwards, sideways and up/down.

SHLEMOFON

The cloth headgear with integrated earphone and microphone for radio communication worn under the helmet of the Sokol suit in the Soyuz spacecraft.

SNOOPY CAP

The American equivalent to the Shlemofon. It's the cloth headgear with the integrated earphone and microphone used for radio communication and worn under the EMU suit helmet. The name comes from the aviator cap that Snoopy wears in the Peanuts cartoons by Charles Schulz.

SOKOL

Pressure suit worn by astronauts flying in the Russian spacecraft Soyuz. An emergency suit, it is designed to sustain an astronaut's life in the event of atmospheric loss in the cabin and cannot be used in space outside a spacecraft.

SOYUZ

Soyuz is the name of the Russian spacecraft, rocket and space program and is the word for union in Russian.

SPACE-TO-GROUND

The radio communication channel used by astronauts and cosmonauts to speak from the ISS to Mission Control Centers around the world.

STS

Space Transportation System. Space Shuttle missions were named STS and then a number. The first NASA space shuttle orbital spaceflight was STS-1. The last Space Shuttle mission was STS-135.

TSUP

The acronym for the Roscomos Russian Mission Control Center in Korolev in the larger Moscow metropolitan area. It's pronounced like "soup."

TVIS

Acronym for Treadmill with Vibration Isolation Stabilization System. This is the special treadmill astronauts use while living on the International Space Station. It's special harness, similar to a backpacker's harness, allows astronauts to adjust the weight load. The harness is attached to the treadmill by two bungees, which is what holds the astronaut down and makes it possible for them to run on the treadmill.

UKSA

Acronym for United Kingdom Space Agency.

WEIGH-OUT

The process of attaching weights and floaters to the Orlan or EMU spacesuits to achieve neutral buoyancy when training underwater.

WHC

Acronym for Waste Hygiene Compartment which is the fancy name for the space toilet.

WHERE TO LEARN MORE

NASA
The official NASA website is at: https://www.nasa.gov/

CANADA SPACE AGENCY
The Canadian Space Agency website has a wealth of video and information about their astronauts and what it's like to live in space. Visit their website at: https://www.asc-csa.gc.ca/eng/astronauts/default.asp

EUROPEAN SPACE AGENCY
Want to learn about the European Space Agency? Want to see who becomes the next ESA astronauts? They just recently opened up applications. Find out the latest on their website: https://www.esa.int/

ROSCOSMOS – RUSSIAN SPACE AGENCY
Learn about the Russian space program and the cosmonauts who have made history on the English version of their official website here: http://en.roscosmos.ru/

JAXA – JAPAN AEROSPACE EXPLORATION AGENCY
Learn more about Japan's Space Agency, the research they are doing on the ISS, their launch vehicles and so much more. Visit their official website here: https://global.jaxa.jp/

ASTRONAUT BIOGRAPHIES
Get all the information you could ever want about NASA astronauts here: https://www.nasa.gov/astronauts

Find out the latest on the ESA astronauts here: http://www.esa.int/Science_Exploration/Human_and_Robotic_Exploration/Astronauts/European_astronauts

Learn about the active and former CSA astronauts here:
https://www.asc-csa.gc.ca/eng/astronauts/canadian/default.asp

NASA LIVE YouTube Streams
NASA has two different livestreams on YouTube, plus a host of
other playlists and videos to see what the astronauts are up to, the
Perseverance Rover on Mars and so much more. Find their official
YouTube channel here: https://www.youtube.com/channel/UCLA_
DiR1FfKNvjuUpBHmylQ

#AskNASA
Have a question for NASA? Use the hashtag #AskNASA on Twitter or
Instagram to ask your question and NASA will answer.

HOW TO PREPARE TO BECOME AN ASTRONAUT
NASA answers this here: https://www.nasa.gov/feature/10-ways-
students-can-prepare-to-beanastronaut

The CSA has lots of useful information about what it takes to be
a CSA astronaut found here: https://www.asc-csa.gc.ca/eng/
astronauts/how-to-become-an-astronaut/default.asp

ESA recently opened up applications to become an ESA astronaut.
Find out what qualities they look for:
https://www.esa.int/Science_Exploration/Human_and_Robotic_
Exploration/Astronauts/How_to_become_an_astronaut

The Japanese Space Agency answers this question here: https://
global.jaxa.jp/article/special/astronaut/yanagawa_e.html

ARTEMIS – SENDING HUMANS TO THE MOON AGAIN
Learn about what NASA is doing to send humans to the Moon again
here: https://www.nasa.gov/specials/artemis/

MARS
Want the latest information on what NASA is doing on Mars with the
Perseverance Rover and *Ingenuity*, the Mars helicopter? Get all the
latest info here: https://mars.nasa.gov/mars2020/

HOW SPACE EXPLORATION BENEFITS US

Want to learn about all the benefits space exploration has had on our lives here on Earth? Learn more here: https://homeandcity.nasa.gov/

VIEW ALL OF THE EXPERIMENTS PERFORMED ON THE ISS

To see and search for all of the experiments that have happened and are happening onboard the space station, visit: https://www.nasa.gov/mission_pages/station/research/experiments/explorer/index.html

QUORA

Quora is a great place to ask questions and find answers about a variety of things, but especially about astronauts and space exploration. There are even a few astronauts and folks who work at NASA who have answered several astronaut-related questions for others that you can read.

PHOTOS AND VIDEOS

Some of the best and most complete collection of photographs taken of the Earth since 1961 can be found and searched for here: https://eol.jsc.nasa.gov/

LIVE VIDEO FROM THE ISS

The live video from the International Space Station that includes views of the crew when they're on-duty, audio conversations between the crew and Mission Control and views of the earth from space at other times can be viewed here: https://www.nasa.gov/multimedia/nasatv/iss_ustream.html

VIEW EARTH LIVE FROM THE INTERNATIONAL SPACE STATION

A camera mounted on the ISS streams live video footage and shows the earth below as it flies by at 5 miles per second or 8 km per second.

Here's where you can see the view of the Earth as seen from the International Space Station: https://www.asc-csa.gc.ca/eng/iss/watch-live.asp

COMMUNICATING WITH THE ISS VIA HAM RADIO
AMATEUR RADIO ON THE INTERNATIONAL SPACE STATION PROGRAM

Learn how it all started, how you can apply to have your group speak to the crew onboard the ISS and what frequencies and call signs to use. Find that all here: https://www.ariss.org/

ASTRONAUTS AND THEIR CALL SIGNS

Get the full list of call signs for astronauts who are, or were at one time, licensed ham radio operators. See it here: https://www.ariss.org/hams-in-space.html

HOW TO HEAR THE INTERNATIONAL SPACE STATION

Find out what equipment you need to hear the ISS, how you can listen online, when to listen and what you can expect to hear at https://amsat-uk.org/beginners/how-to-hear-the-iss/

RECOMMENDED ASTRONAUT BOOKS
Books Written *By* Astronauts:

An Astronaut's Guide to Life on Earth: What Going to Space Taught Me About Ingenuity, Determination, and Being Prepared for Anything by Chris Hadfield

Ask an Astronaut: My Guide to Life in Space by Tim Peake

Diary of an Apprentice Astronaut by Samantha Cristoforetti

Endurance: My Year in Space. A Lifetime of Discovery by Scott Kelly

Handprints on Hubble: An Astronaut's Story of Invention by Kathryn Sullivan

How to Astronaut: An Insider's Guide to Leaving Planet Earth by Terry Virts

Go For Orbit: One of America's First Women Astronauts Finds Her Space by Rhea Seddon

Through the Glass Ceiling to the Stars: The Story of the First American Woman to Command a Space Mission by Col. Eileen M. Collins

Books Written *About* Astronauts:

Almost Astronauts: 13 Women Who Dared to Dream by Tanya Lee Stone

A Man on the Moon: The Voyages of the Apollo Astronauts by Andrew Chaikin

Fallen Astronauts: Heroes Who Died Reaching for the Moon by Colin Burgess and Kate Doolan

The Mercury 13: The Untold Story of Thirteen American Women and the Dream of Space Flight by Martha Ackermann

Packing for Mars: The Curious Science Of Life In Space by Mary Roach

The Astronaut's Cookbook: Tales, Recipes, and More by Charles T. Bourland

RECOMMENDED ASTRONAUT WEBSITES

First British Astronaut, Helen Sharman
  Read her fascinating FAQs and learn how you can book Helen to come and speak to your group. Details at https://www.helensharman.uk/frequently-asked-questions/

First Canadian to Walk in Space, Chris Hadfield
  Learn about Colonel Hadfield, find out about his latest book, learn about events in your area and sign up to get the latest at: https://chrishadfield.ca/

First Female Pilot and Female Commander of a space shuttle, Eileen M. Collins
  Find out more about former astronaut and retired U.S. Air Force colonel, Eileen Collins. Learn more about her new book and read what she says about what it takes to become an astronaut. Details found on her official website: http://marklarson.com/eileencollins/one.html

First American Woman to Walk in Space, Kathy Sullivan
  Sullivan has been to space and the bottom of the ocean. Read her blog and learn about her podcast where she talks about her historic experiences: https://kathysullivanastronaut.com/

RECOMMENDED ASTRONAUT-RELATED PODCASTS

ESA Explores
Get behind the scenes with the European Space Agency and find out how they train their astronauts, the science behind the ISS and what it will take to go to Mars.

Houston, We Have a Podcast
The official podcast of the Johnson Space Center in Houston, Texas where the host talks about all things space and how it works to get humans there. Lots of interviews with guests that talk spacesuits, artificial gravity and what it will take to get humans back to the Moon and to Mars.

Kathy Sullivan Explores
Astronaut Kathy Sullivan is the only person to have both walked in space and visited the deepest point in the ocean. In her new podcast she shares unique insights and perspectives about her experiences in space and in the ocean. She is also joined by a variety of guests which always leads to fascinating discussions.

Space and Things
A weekly podcast that explores all things about space. Learn about spacesuits, top tips for visiting Space Center Houston, how to talk to someone in space via Ham Radio and so much more. It's presented by historian Emily Carney and space nerd Dave Giles. More details at: https://www.spaceandthingspodcast.com

BBC World Service – Space
Listen to a collection of radio documentary programs that talk about all things space. Episodes cover what happen the day the Skylab space station fell to Earth, what it will take to get a woman on the Moon and the future of space flight. Get all of the episodes here: https://www.bbc.co.uk/programmes/p03bv899/episodes/player

MECO
MECO stands for Main Engine Cut Off and is a podcast by Anthony Colangelo. With over 200 episodes, you'll find topics, news and

opinions about space tourism, Starship news, China's space station and so much more. Find it here: https://mainenginecutoff.com/podcast

Are We There Yet?

Listen to weekly space news updates and interviews with astronauts, engineers and visionaries by space reporter Brendan Byrne. Find it on Spotify and Apple Podcasts.

LEARN SOMETHING?
PLEASE LEAVE A REVIEW

If you enjoyed this book, please share your thoughts in a REVIEW. Your sincere feedback is really helpful and I would love to hear from you!

Please leave a quick review at your favorite retailer!

Thank you so very much!

DON'T FORGET YOUR BONUS

As a **special bonus** and as a **thank you** for purchasing this book, I'm giving you a free download of my first award-winning book:

"So You Think You Know CANADA, Eh? Fascinating Fun Facts and Trivia about Canada for the Entire Family."

How much DO YOU REALLY KNOW about Canada?
Discover fascinating fun facts and trivia and test your knowledge of Canada and quiz your friends.

It's all FREE.

Download your bonus fun fact e-book here:

https://bit.ly/astronautbook2-bonus

Enjoy!

INDEX

ABOUT THE AUTHOR

Marianne Jennings is a self-proclaimed adventure craver and an adventure addict. She goes on crazy adventures with people she's never met, isn't afraid to try new things like learning to sail in the middle of the Atlantic Ocean even though she's prone to seasickness and proudly holds the title of favorite aunt to her ten nieces and nephews. Marianne is a lover of new foods, new experiences and wants to be remembered for being kind and generous.

She loves facts and trivia like astronauts love drinking Tang and flying like Superman. To help introduce other places, people, and cultures to others, she likes to share interesting and fun facts that are entertaining and memorable.

If you'd like to learn more or join her mailing list, you can connect with Marianne at https://knowledgenuggetbooks.com or on Instagram @knowledgenuggetbooks.

ALSO BY MARIANNE JENNINGS

Everything About Astronauts Vol 1

Fascinating Fun Facts and Trivia about Astronauts for Teens and Adults

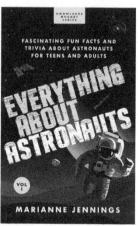

Volume 1 is jam packed with over 600 fun facts and little-known tidbits.

Learn what it takes to become an astronaut, little-known facts about famous astronauts and a few surprising facts about items brought to the Moon and back and a few items that were left there; some on purpose and some on accident.

Available as e-book and paperback.
Find it wherever fine books are sold – online and in stores.

• • •

2020 Readers' Favorite International Gold Medal Winner

So You Think You Know CANADA, Eh?

Fascinating Fun Facts and Trivia about Canada for the Entire Family

Available as an e-book, paperback and audiobook.

Find it wherever fine fun fact books are sold – online and in stores.

Made in the USA
Las Vegas, NV
26 June 2024

91512255R00164